THE HUNTERS
AND THE HENWIFE

A Play for Children

THE HUNTERS
AND THE HENWIFE

NICHOLAS STUART GRAY

Illustrated by

JOAN
JEFFERSON FARJEON

822/GRA *Geoffrey Cumberlege*
OXFORD UNIVERSITY PRESS
1954

Oxford University Press, Amen House, London E.C.4
GLASGOW   NEW YORK   TORONTO   MELBOURNE   WELLINGTON
BOMBAY   CALCUTTA   MADRAS   KARACHI   CAPE TOWN   IBADAN
Geoffrey Cumberlege, Publisher to the University

First published 1954

*Printed in Great Britain by Richard Clay and Company, Ltd.,
Bungay, Suffolk*

For Louise

with my love and admiration

CHARACTERS

REYNARD

RUFUS

THE HENWIFE

BARON WILLIAM

BRIONY

POPPI

BAT

HEMLOCK, THE SORCERER

SETTINGS

ACT ONE

Scene 1   In the forest, on Unicorn Mountain
Scene 2   Inside the Henwife's cottage

ACT TWO

Scene 1   Under a tree in the forest
Scene 2   The Sorcerer's hunting-lodge

ACT THREE

Scene 1   Inside the Henwife's cottage
Scene 2   The Sorcerer's castle

TIME

Once, on a night of full moon . . .

IN THE FOREST, ON UNICORN MOUNTAIN

In a small clearing lies a log fallen from the tall trees above. At the back the twilight sky can be seen through branches. The trees have curiously twisted trunks, and the colours are rather odd.

On the log two huntsmen are sitting, chins in hands, staring at a pile of twigs. Their fire will not light. RUFUS *is red-haired, rather good looking, and has a fairly decisive manner.* REYNARD *is dark, vague, and much given to dithering. He proceeds to do this almost immediately, by peering nervously over his shoulder.*

REYNARD. Don't like it.

> [RUFUS *stoops forward to blow into the fire.*
> REYNARD *looks round again, and shivers.*]

I've got the twitters—I don't like this place. I don't—
I don't.

> [RUFUS *breaks a twig across his knee, and* REY-
> NARD *starts.*]

What a thing to do!

> [*He looks round him again, and* RUFUS *re-lays the
> fire.*]

Rufus. I say, Rufus . . .

RUFUS. Umm?

REYNARD. I wish you'd talk.

RUFUS. You talk enough for ten.

REYNARD. I do it for company. I'm lonely. I hate this
place.

RUFUS. You've said that thirty times in the last five
minutes.

REYNARD. And I'll say it a thousand times in the next
five.

RUFUS. You couldn't.

REYNARD. Could.

RUFUS. Couldn't!

REYNARD. Could.

RUFUS. Couldn't! Enough! You'd argue all night.

REYNARD. That would be better than sitting in silence,
just looking at the creepy forest, and listening to the
dew falling. It would be better than that, it would.

RUFUS. It wouldn't.

REYNARD. It would!

RUFUS. I'm not playing.

> [*He blows at the fire again, while* REYNARD
> *fidgets uneasily.*]

REYNARD [*at last*]. Let's move on, Rufus. Let's go and look for the Baron. He can't be far away.

RUFUS. He can.

REYNARD. He can't . . . no, I'm *not*. . . . I mean, I heard his horn a minute ago. Let's go and find him.

RUFUS. What for? He told us to stay here. Help me with the fire, Reynard. My lord will be angry when he comes.

REYNARD [*gloomily*]. He'll be livid. No deer in the forest for his arrows. No bird in the sky for his falcon to stoop at. And now, no fire. He'll blame us.

RUFUS. Well, if you'd give me a hand, instead of dithering like a demented dabchick . . . it would light.

REYNARD. It wouldn't.

RUFUS. It w . . .
    [*He pushes* REYNARD *off the log.*]
Tt! Why we brought you with us is a mystery to me. You're a dead loss as a huntsman. Lord William must have been dreaming when he summoned you.

REYNARD. He was in a hurry.
    [*In the distance, a hunting-horn is blown. A long call.*]

RUFUS. There's his horn.
    [*He raises his own horn to his lips, and blows a reply.*]
He'll know where we are, anyway.

REYNARD. More than I do. I hate this forest. It's so quiet; Rufus, it's dead. All day there's been no living thing to be seen in it. And now, it's getting darker, and darker . . .

RUFUS. It's nearly night, you fool.

REYNARD. That's what worries me.

[3]

RUFUS. Huh?

REYNARD. The darkness is creeping slowly over this dead forest. We've all heard strange legends about Unicorn Mountain, and the forest on its slopes. If nothing moves among the trees by day, what may move here in the dark?

[*A pause. They both look round them, nervously. They shiver.* RUFUS *pulls himself together.*]

RUFUS. I do think you're beastly.

[*They get closer together, glancing uneasily about them. The horn sounds again, nearer, and they both jump.*]

That was my lord's horn. [*Pause.*] Wasn't it, Reynard?

REYNARD. Er . . . yes . . . I hope! Rufus, I'm frightened.

RUFUS. You're not.

REYNARD. I am.

RUFUS. You're . . . well, so am I.

[*In the fading light, the* HENWIFE *enters. A straight-backed old lady, with a serene, ageless face, and slanted eyes. She wears a cloak of hen-feathers, and carries a white, fluffy hen on her shoulder. The two huntsmen are looking away, and do not see her approach. She comes near, and looks at them.*]

HENWIFE. You should not be here.

[*The* HUNTSMEN *stiffen, without turning, and shut their eyes. After a moment,* REYNARD *nudges* RUFUS.]

REYNARD. Who spoke, Rufus?

RUFUS. Can't see. Got my eyes shut.

REYNARD. Be brave.

HENWIFE. You do look silly.

[4]

RUFUS. I suppose we must. [*He opens his eyes.*] Oh, . . .
er . . . hallo.

HENWIFE. By all means, hallo to you, young man!
May I ask why you are standing here like a pair of
loobies? Human strangers on the mountain, with the
night just coming on! And . . . mercy me, tonight of
all nights! It will be full moon tonight. . . . *What*
are you doing here?

REYNARD. You may well ask, Mistress Feathers.
We're trying to light a fire, that's what. Like the
Baron told us.

HENWIFE. Another? Another stranger here?

REYNARD. Well, don't look so very put out. I didn't
like *coming* here . . . and I don't like *being* here . . .
and I wish I *wasn't* here!

HENWIFE. You must immediately call your lord, and
make him leave the forest.

REYNARD. He'd not stir an inch for our bidding.
You don't know our young Baron, that's clear. He's
set on his own ideas, and stubborn as a mule, and a
fair terror for hunting. . . .

HENWIFE. Hunting?

REYNARD. He's always at it.

HENWIFE. Hunting?

RUFUS. He's grand at it.

HENWIFE. Hunting on Unicorn Mountain! With the
moon rising full. Pray tell me, what does he propose
hunting?

RUFUS. We don't rightly know, mistress. He hunted
everything down in his own country, and then he
heard tales of the Mountain. . . .

REYNARD. Strange tales, of stranger beasts. So he
must needs come riding up here, wishing to hunt

[5]

something other than the known beasts of his own valleys.

HENWIFE. Is he crazed?

REYNARD [*nervously*]. In what way?

HENWIFE. It is no right sport for a man to chase and kill the beasts. Cruel, and inexcusable! To hunt for food is one thing . . . but for sport! That is brainless savagery.

REYNARD. I'm not putting that to the Baron! We're only his servants, mistress.

HENWIFE. Are human beings as brutal as the monsters of the forest?

[*The hunting-horn is heard again, fairly near. A new call.*]

RUFUS. He's coming. And he's found no quarry yet, by that call.

HENWIFE. He'll find none here. If he stays in this forest, after moonrise, it's he will be the quarry . . . and you! And you!

RUFUS. } Us?
REYNARD. } Me?

HENWIFE. All! Yourselves will be the hunted. And I dare not tell what will be hunting you.

[*A pause. The* HUNTSMEN *look at each other.*]

REYNARD. Oh.

HENWIFE. There's another who hunts on the Mountain. I've said all I can, for it is dangerous to speak of it. You must make your lord leave the forest . . . force him, if need be . . . for you've little time to lose, if you wish to save your lives.

WILLIAM [*off*]. Hey! Hey, there!

REYNARD [*starting violently*]. Oh, my nerves!

RUFUS [*calls*]. Here, my lord!

[6]

REYNARD. You speak to him, Mistress Feathers. He may listen to you, though I think it most unlikely. Oh dear, I wish I was in bed with a cold!

[*Enter* LORD WILLIAM. *He is dark, and tall, and magnificently handsome. His voice is deep and ringing. He is young. His brain—but it would be kinder not to go any further. He carries a great bow, and his hunting-horn, and sheath of arrows, are slung across his shoulders.*]

WILLIAM. I have lost my falcon.

REYNARD. My lord, we must tell you . . .

WILLIAM. I have lost Finian, my falcon. He must be found.

REYNARD. You see, it's nearly moonrise, my lord. . . .

WILLIAM. I know that. How else could we find Finian? We'll wait till then, and go to the place where I lost him. He'll be asleep in the tree where he flew. I was rash to loose him so late.

REYNARD. Wait till moonrise?

HENWIFE [*moving forward*]. This will not do, at all. My good young man, if you have any sense whatever . . . which, from the look of you, you should have . . . you will instantly go home, and take these two idiots with you.

REYNARD. The lady's right, sir.

WILLIAM. Make yourself clearer, madam.

HENWIFE. Good gracious, I'm not invisible, am I?

[*She glances at her hand, and sighs with relief.*]

No, of course not, the moon's not up yet.

WILLIAM [*smiling*]. And if it were?

HENWIFE. Anything could happen. Sir, I thought at first that you looked sensible . . . don't be sillier than you look! Leave this forest before the moon rises.

Before the woods wake to magic . . . before the things
of the night take power from the darkness . . .

REYNARD. Before long!

WILLIAM. What is this rigmarole of nonsense?

HENWIFE. I was mistaken in you, you're slow. But
even fools value their lives. Look at these two.

REYNARD. Yes, do, my lord.

HENWIFE. They're very much afraid. *They* believed
my warnings.

RUFUS. It's as the lady says, my lord. This forest has
frightened me.

REYNARD. And I'm scared stiff.

WILLIAM. Oh, you! You're always starting at shadows.

HENWIFE. There are some shadows well worth starting
at, let me tell you.

WILLIAM. And let me tell you, madam, that all this
talk of magic and the moon leaves me more than cold.
It is arrant nonsense, and you are old enough not to
tell such fairy-tales to grown men.

HENWIFE. Grown men! Pack of silly babies! You'll
feel young enough, I promise you, if you stay here
much longer! Grown men! I'd like to slap you!

[*The* BARON *laughs amiably, and crosses to her
side.*]

WILLIAM. You go home, old lady, if you're nervous
of the night-winds. You must not fear for us. We'll
not catch colds.

HENWIFE. You'll not catch anything! But you may be
caught.

WILLIAM. Enough, enough! Take your hen home to
her roost, and have your supper, and forget your
fairy-tales. Living in the forest has made you fanciful.

HENWIFE. Oh, you silly boy! Silly baby! Certainly,

[8]

I'll go and leave you to your folly, since you can do nothing but laugh at my warnings. I'll try no more. Baby! You'll cry for help when it's too late. Foolish boy . . . oh, so foolish . . .

> [*As she goes muttering away among the trees, the* BARON *laughs again, and calls to her.*]

WILLIAM. Sleep well, lady, and have no nightmares!

HENWIFE [*turning*]. All the nightmares in the forest will be with you, young man.

> [*She goes off. The* BARON *turns to his huntsmen, and shouts at them suddenly, irritated by their doleful faces.*]

WILLIAM. Stop beating about the bush!

> [*They both start violently, and* REYNARD *sits down hard.*]

REYNARD [*weakly*]. Never touched it.

WILLIAM. You're hungry, and you're tired, and you want to turn for home. Well, why can't you say so? Instead of listening to a string of childish nonsense about magic from a mad and solitary old woman? Why pretend you're afraid of an ordinary, common-or-garden forest?

REYNARD. It's the least common forest I've ever seen.

WILLIAM. Hold your silly tongue! Rufus, what are *you* playing at? You're no coward.

RUFUS. My lord . . .

REYNARD. Look! Look!

> [*The moon begins to rise. Very slowly it lifts from behind the trees at the back. And the light begins to change, but not to ordinary moonlight.*]

WILLIAM. Well, what of it?

REYNARD. The moon is rising.

WILLIAM. We've seen it do so many times before.

REYNARD. Not from Unicorn Mountain, my lord.

WILLIAM. It's the last time you come hunting with me, Reynard. You're completely idiotic. Rufus, get that fire alight. It will be an hour before there's light enough to see the falcon. The horses are all right over there? Very well, I'll rest. You'd better do the same, from the haggard looks of you.

> [*He lies down on his cloak, left, and leans on an elbow to say;*

And no more nonsense, do you hear! Wake me in an hour, and don't trouble yourselves to invent more baby-tales. I've no intention of being told that the moon has wrought magic in the forest . . . that there are strange creatures round us . . . or that the trees have changed their shapes. You must follow my example, and believe only what you see.

> [*He drops his head into the crook of his arm, and lies still. The light changes a little. A pause.*]

REYNARD [*rigid with fear*]. Look!

RUFUS. Where?

REYNARD. Eyes.

> [*Up in the branches of the tree above him, are two green eyes blinking out of the shadow.*]

Strange creatures around us . . .

> [*The light changes to a greater degree, and the trees relax their arms, with a curious sighing sound.*]

RUFUS. The trees have changed their shapes.

REYNARD. Wake the Baron.

RUFUS. I dare not. Light the fire.

REYNARD. My hands are shaking. You do it.

> [*RUFUS stoops over the fire, but recoils as a green spark glows in the pile of twigs.*]

Don't do that, Rufus!

[10]

RUFUS. It was not I.

[*The fire lights, without assistance, and the flames are oddly coloured. The two* HUNTSMEN *move away from it sideways.*]

It's not my idea of a nice fire.

REYNARD. It was your idea to light it. Wake the Baron!

RUFUS. He'll not be convinced. He's a proper handful once he gets an idea in his head, and he's made up his mind. He'll never go home, now.

REYNARD. Don't say such things!

RUFUS [*turning up, quickly*]. What's that!

REYNARD. Don't. [*A squeak of terror.*]

RUFUS. Over there . . . what is it? What are you?

A VOICE [*off*]. Me.

ANOTHER VOICE. Us.

[*The two* HUNTSMEN *look nervously at one another.*]

REYNARD. Well, go away.

[*Someone laughs, and then* BRIONY *enters. She is a young girl with fair hair, long and straight to her shoulders. Dressed in green, and bare-footed. She has a quaint pointed face, with scarlet lips. A gentle, and unusual creature, with a tender voice.*]

BRIONY. How rude of you to say ' Go away '.

REYNARD. Are you . . . a witch?

RUFUS. Give over, Reynard, do! Excuse him, please, mistress; he's not himself tonight.

BRIONY. What an odd fire you have there, to be sure.

RUFUS. It sort of . . . went like that . . . er . . .

BRIONY. My name is Briony. I live here, you know.

REYNARD. Here? Then you *are* a . . .

BRIONY. I'm no witch. I never had any ambition to

make magic . . . though my mother is quite good at it. White magic, of course . . . and only the simplest kind. My mother is the Henwife. Have you met her?

RUFUS. I think so, yes, Mistress Briony.

REYNARD. If you aren't a . . . well, what are you doing alone here, by moonlight?

BRIONY. I'm not alone. Come here, Poppi! Yes, you may come now. He's so friendly, you know. I forbid him to speak to anyone till I have spoken first.

RUFUS. Who is Poppi?

BRIONY. Come here, dear. They are quite human.
    [*Enter* POPPI. *He is little, with a scarlet, furry tummy, and dog's paws. A short, red tail, and a golden rain of scales over his back. His ears are large and fluffy, and the face is like that of a friendly child. He looks inquiringly round a tree.*]

REYNARD. *What* is Poppi?

BRIONY. A puppy Salamander. He's a cross between a Salamander and a fire-dog, aren't you, dear?

POPPI. Yis.

BRIONY. You may talk to these. They are not the monsters of Hemlock in disguise. They do not wear his badge. Oh, I should not say his name!

POPPI. I like 'em!
    [*He is frisking from* RUFUS *to* REYNARD, *in the friendliest way imaginable.*]
    Nice! Nice! Nice!

REYNARD. Oh . . . ah . . . yes . . . splendid!

RUFUS. Good Poppi. Good girl.

POPPI. Boy.

RUFUS. What?

BRIONY. He's a boy Salamander, you silly thing.

RUFUS. You called her . . . him . . . it, Poppi.

POPPI. That's my name. Short for Poppi . . . Poppi . . .

BRIONY. Short for Popocatepetl. The volcano, you know.

POPPI. My people came from there, once. In the beginning.

BRIONY. It was ages before Salamanders could live out of fire.

POPPI. Nice fire.

> [*He goes and sits on the fire. Smoke rises round him.*]

RUFUS. Steady!

BRIONY. You'll put it out, Poppi. Do get up, dear, we must go now. My mother will be displeased that I have spoken with you. I should not be out in the forest after moonrise. The bad things are all leaving their lairs by then. You might have been servants to Hemlock . . . but you are not wearing snakes for sign of it. All his servants wear snakes, you know. But I shouldn't speak of him. Oh dear, Mother is always warning me.

RUFUS. We don't belong in the forest at all. Our master sleeps, over there.

REYNARD. Who is Hemlock?

BRIONY. I must whisper. He is the black Sorcerer. He lives in a castle up among the mists on the peak of the mountain. He is master only of bad magic, and we are all afraid of him when the darkness comes, and he is hunting.

RUFUS. You'd better cut along, my girl. Is your home far?

BRIONY. Over there. My mother has set little barricades of white magic round her cottage . . . so that we are safe there, while we are all together. She and I, and Poppi, and Bat, the Sorcerer's son . . .

[13]

REYNARD. His son? With you? Is that safe?

BRIONY. Yes. Mother knows how to protect him from his wicked father. She wants to stop Bat becoming a Black Magician, and to keep him safe with us, until he can learn to have a real heart.

RUFUS. I don't understand.

BRIONY. It's perfectly simple. But I mustn't stay to explain. It is getting very late indeed. Forgive me for chattering so. I hope my Mother will not be anxious. Good-bye.

[*She runs out, waving her hand and laughing.*]

RUFUS [*to* POPPI]. Well, you'd better gallop along, and look after her.

REYNARD. He *has* put the fire out.

POPPI. Oh, I'm bad! Nasty Poppi! I've put the fire out. I'll put it in again. I'll run round it, and sing to it . . . a very hot, hot fiery song . . . and it will light again. You'll see.

[*He runs round the fire, singing. While he does so, smoke and odd colours show in the fire, with cracklings, and explosions that are almost in time to his song.*]

Round the fire, run, run,
Singing flame, singing sun.
Singing heat, glow, haze,
Melt, burn, furnace blaze;
Rise smoke, billowing,
Kindle fire, while I sing.

[*The fire bursts into coloured flames, and during the previous excitement, the* BARON *has awakened. He watches, puzzled, for a few moments, and still half-asleep.*]

WILLIAM. What *is* going on!

[14]

RUFUS. Well . . . er . . .

REYNARD. Just . . . just lighting the fire, my lord.

WILLIAM [*rising quickly*]. What is that creature?

POPPI. Poppi. It's Poppi. Hallo, who are you? Nice.

> [POPPI *runs to the* BARON, *and fawns on him.*]

WILLIAM. A hunt at last. Here is a quarry.

RUFUS. No. No, my lord!

REYNARD. This is Poppi.

WILLIAM. It's an animal, of sorts. Get away, you creature. You shall be hunted. The moon is clear enough for me to loose an arrow.

POPPI. No, I'm Poppi. I'm friends with you. Look.

> [*He rubs his head against the* BARON'S *knee.*]

I lit your fire for you. Don't push me away, like that . . . you'll make me cross. And if I get cross, I get ever so hot. . . .

RUFUS. You see, my lord, it talks!

WILLIAM. I came here to hunt strange quarry.

RUFUS. You'd better go, Poppi.

REYNARD. Shoo! Shoo!

POPPI. I'm beginning to sizzle! My tail is getting hot!

REYNARD. Well, sizzle along home. Ow!

> [*He has pushed the* SALAMANDER, *and scorched his hand.*]

POPPI. I'm cross! I'm cross! You've burnt your hand on me, 'cos I'm cross, and hot . . .

RUFUS. Home, Poppi . . . shoo . . .

> [*From the distance, a cry echoes through the trees, faintly.*]

Was that . . . Briony?

WILLIAM [*firmly*]. It was an owl. Drive that animal away, and give him a hundred paces start.

[15]

RUFUS. Oh, go, Poppi! Never mind sizzling! Find Briony. You were her guard, and we've delayed you here. . . .

POPPI. Yis, I'll find her . . . but I'm still very, very hot!

> [*He dashes off, shouting;*

I can run faster than foxes!

> [*The* BARON *raises his great bow, one hand to his arrows.*]

WILLIAM. He is clear in the moonlight, down the glade. When he reaches that dead tree . . .

RUFUS. No, my lord!

> [*The* BARON *fits an arrow to the bow, and shoots, more swiftly than the eye can follow . . . as* RUFUS *tries to stop him.*]

REYNARD. Missed!

WILLIAM [*to* RUFUS]. Your fault, fool!

> [*The light changes, and the slanted eyes in the shadows of the tree, begin to blink again.*]

REYNARD. Look there!

WILLIAM. Nothing but a trick of the moonlight.

> [*A voice speaks from the tree, coldly and without anger, without soul.*]

VOICE. Lord from human lands, you have challenged Unicorn Mountain. The challenge is accepted. Your huntsmen are blundering nearer and nearer to a spell that has been lying around, doing nothing, for centuries. A spell that was almost forgotten . . . until now.

> [RUFUS *and* REYNARD *have been backing away from the shadowy voice, until they are close against a tree opposite. Now, this tree suddenly breaks into a flicker of tiny red lights, that vanish and re-appear*

[16]

warningly, here and there on the trunk. It also hisses.
RUFUS *goes off quietly into the shadows, offstage.*
REYNARD *stands stiffly against the tree, staring.*]
They have touched against the spell. The forest has
answered your challenge.

[*A pause. The* BARON *shrugs his shoulders.*]

WILLIAM. A trick of the echoes. There's nothing in
magic.

REYNARD. Too much for my liking.

WILLIAM. Pull yourselves together, do. Take a sup of
wine to hearten you. It's light enough to search for
Finian, now, and if I sight other quarry, I shall not
miss again. Magic? I'll not believe such ancient
nonsense. Where is Rufus?

REYNARD. Here, my lord.

WILLIAM. Where?

REYNARD. I'm here. I am Rufus, my lord.

WILLIAM. Don't play the fool. You're Reynard.

REYNARD. Yes, sir, and I'm Rufus, too.

WILLIAM. Is this a joke?

REYNARD. Not on my part. We've walked into a very
powerful spell, my lord. And Rufus and I have got
rolled up into one person . . . and here we are, both
of us.

WILLIAM. Stop this! You're Reynard, only.

REYNARD. Yes, I'm Reynard. And I'm Rufus, too.
(*Ru.*) That's right, my lord. I'm Rufus, and I'm
Reynard, too. We're both here. Do you see.

WILLIAM. Frankly, no.

REYNARD (*Ru.*) I'm Rufus.
Be quiet, I'll speak!
(*Ru.*) No, you won't.
Yes, I will.

[17]

(*Ru.*) Won't!
Will!
(*Ru.*) Won't!

> [*Poor* REYNARD *is arguing fiercely now, with himself, in two voices, one of which has distinctly the accents of* RUFUS.]

REYNARD. (*Ru.*) Shut up, Reynard, do! Let me speak. We're both here, sir, in one body. It's magic.

WILLIAM. Nonsense.

> [*A pause. The* BARON *shrugs his shoulders.*]

You must have been standing in something.

CURTAIN

INSIDE THE HENWIFE'S COTTAGE

The cottage is very cosy, and lit by firelight. There are low rafters, with white hens roosting on them. On the back of a tall wooden chair is another hen, asleep, with her head under her wing. And, by the fire, a hen in a basket. There is a low door, left, and a little crooked window upstage of the fire, right. At the back of the cottage are shelves with crocks and jugs, with strings of onions, odd tiny doors of cupboards, and here and there hens, roosting. The HENWIFE'S *cloak of feathers hangs behind the door, left.*

The HENWIFE *herself is lifting the lid of a big round pot on the fire. Steam rises from it, as she tastes the contents from a ladle.*

BAT, *the son of the enchanter, is sitting in the wooden chair, at the other side of the oak table. He is young and handsome, but he has no heart. His mood varies between childish malice*

[19]

*and something wild and strange. On the surface, his hair is
green, but yellow underneath. A very decorative snake coils
round his waist, so that its head lies across his breast.*

HENWIFE. Nearly ready. Pass me the salt, Bat.

BAT. Why?

HENWIFE. Because I ask you to. Now, Bat, be a good
boy. It's to make your supper nice.

> [BAT *looks at her, then laughs, and rising slowly he
> crosses to her, with a small jar from the table.*]

Thank you.

> [*About to shake some of the contents of the jar into the
> pot, she stops suddenly.* BAT *laughs, quietly.*]

What is it! Ginger? Ginger in the porridge! You
horrid creature, what shall I do with you! You stop
laughing this very minute, do you hear?

BAT. If I wish to laugh, I must.

HENWIFE. You've no heart at all.

BAT. That is so.

HENWIFE. Oh, Bat . . . *that's* not a thing to laugh at.
It's a dreadful state to be in.

> [*She puts the ginger back on the table, and picks up
> another jar, this time of salt.*]

BAT. You say it is unnatural to be heartless, but it
does not in any way disturb me.

HENWIFE. I've tried so hard to make you understand.
Ever since I met you in the forest . . . gathering
thunder-bolts for your father . . . I've kept you here
safely to see if I could help you. And sometimes I
think you are becoming more human . . . and sometimes that I can do nothing for you. That I should
let you go back to your father.

BAT. I have no wish to return to the castle.

HENWIFE. Do you mean that you like being here, with us? Bat, oh, Bat . . . do you love us a little at last, my dear? Have you the beginnings of a heart?

BAT. I mean that I am afraid of my father.

HENWIFE [*disappointed*]. Is that all?

> [*She sits down by the fire, and strokes the hen in the basket.*]

Perhaps you may learn in time. We must keep on trying. [*She sings softly;*
> The cottage is warm, the fire is bright,
> Who would want to go out in the night?
> Who would want moonlight, and magic, and fear,
> When this is so cosy, and home is here.

> [*A thought strikes her, and she looks anxiously at* BAT.]

Bat, you know you mustn't go out of this cottage tonight? It's full moon.

BAT. Full moon is best.

HENWIFE. Oh, mercy me, you silly boy, do have a little sense! Your father is at the height of his power, then. Now, promise me you'll not go out in the forest tonight.

BAT. Maybe.

HENWIFE. Tiresome creature! You *must* promise. Your father will try hard to get you back tonight. You know how cruel he is? You know how much you fear him? He has ordered you to run away from here, and you've disobeyed . . . what do you think will happen to you, if he gets you to the castle again?

BAT. I'll not go there.

HENWIFE. Then promise me you won't leave the cottage tonight, or he may take you there, whether you like it or not.

BAT. Very well, I promise.

HENWIFE. See that you keep your word. Now pass me the ladle.

> [*She lifts the lid of the pot again, sniffing at the steam, and holding out her hand behind her.* BAT *gives her a little black hearth-brush, and she nearly stirs the porridge with it, but sees it in time.*]

Bat! You wicked boy! And the brush all over ashes! Hold out your hand.

BAT [*laughing again*]. No, indeed.

HENWIFE. Yes, indeed. You're incorrigible ! Hold out your hand, this minute.

> [*He is taller than she, but she looks so fierce that he holds out his hand. She smacks at it with the brush, but the hand is quickly withdrawn, and she smacks her skirt instead.*]

How dare you laugh at me so !

BAT. Now what a temper you're in. And look at the smudge on your skirt.

> [*He points, and the* HENWIFE *slaps his wrist. He stops laughing, suddenly.*]

[*Taken aback.*] You hit me!

HENWIFE. And about time, too. Now, no sulking. We'll say no more about it. And supper's nearly ready. I do wonder where the others are? It's getting late.

> [*She goes to the window, and looks out.* BAT *still sulks.*]

BAT. You hurt me.

HENWIFE. Oh, it's after moonrise! I hadn't realized that. Mercy me, and Briony not back yet. Where is the girl?

BAT [*inspecting his wrist*]. I can still see the mark.

[22]

HENWIFE. She ought to be here. I've told her often enough not to stay out late in the forest.

[*She opens the window, and calls anxiously;*
Briony! She should be safe with Poppi. The ugly things are afraid of him, when he gets angry, and red-hot. He'll bring her safely home . . . he *must*. Briony! Oh, my, this is most worrying.

[*She crosses to the door, and lifts down her feather cloak.*]

I can't leave you here by yourself, Bat. Your father will come and take you, if you are left alone. You must come with me.

BAT. I won't.

HENWIFE. I'm anxious, dear. The moon is up . . . she has never stayed away so late, before. Do hurry.

BAT. No. You hit me.

HENWIFE. Don't be childish! Briony may be in danger . . . you wouldn't want that . . . you *like* her . . .

BAT. I like no one.

HENWIFE. And Poppi . . . you know how he loves you.

BAT. Poppi loves everyone. He's very stupid.

HENWIFE [*riled*]. That's better than being callous and cruel!

BAT. I was born without a heart.

HENWIFE. You're doing very little to acquire one. And what you say is untrue. You had one once, but it is numbed. Oh, my dear, I implore you to come with me.

[*She goes to him, and puts her hands on his shoulders, but before he can make up his mind, the door opens and* POPPI *rushes gaily into the room.*]

POPPI. I'm back! I'm safe! I've escaped!

HENWIFE. Escaped! From what?

C [23]

POPPI. Nice Bat . . . nice! Mother Henwife, I'm safe!

HENWIFE. Where is Briony, Poppi? Where is she?

POPPI. Isn't she here? The Huntsmen told me to go and find her, and I thought she'd be here . . . so I came home.

HENWIFE. Are those Huntsmen still in the forest?

POPPI. They tried to shoot me. But I ran, and ran! Fast . . . faster . . . fastest! And I got back safe to you.

HENWIFE. But my daughter is not back safe.

POPPI. Not?

HENWIFE. And they shot at you? Then all the magic in the forest is roused. It will be dreadful in the forest, tonight. And Briony out there . . .

BAT [*carelessly*]. She can run, too.

HENWIFE. It's easier to outrun an arrow, than to outrun magic.

[*She goes to the door.*]

POPPI. I'll come with you.

HENWIFE. No. Stay here, with Bat. He must not be left alone, or he will be taken prisoner.

POPPI. Then I'll look after him. Nice Bat.

HENWIFE. Listen to me, Poppi. Now, carefully. If the Sorcerer comes here, looking for his son, he will offer you two gold pieces. You must refuse them, do you understand? Whatever he threatens, you must not sell Bat to him.

POPPI. Sell Bat? The idea!

BAT. For two gold pieces? I'm worth more than two.

HENWIFE. That's a matter of opinion. And remember your promise. You're not to leave the hut. I won't be long. She cannot be far away.

[*She opens the door, left, and calls again;*
Briony!

[24]

[*She folds her cloak round her, and turns to the others.*]

For mercy's sake, remember what I've told you!

[*The* HENWIFE *goes out, and closes the door after her.*]

POPPI. I hope Briony isn't lost.

BAT. She'll be safe enough.

POPPI [*relieved*]. Oh, then that's all right. Bat . . . Bat . . . nice Bat, tell me some more magic. Teach me some more spells, do.

BAT. The Henwife told me not to.

POPPI. She said you weren't to teach me spiteful magic. But I can never remember the nasty ones. [*He tries.*] No, it's no good, I just can't.

BAT. You're stupid.

POPPI. Yis, I know.

BAT. I taught you how to make the hens fall off their perches.

POPPI. Yis, and that was funny. But Mother Henwife said it was spiteful, and so I forgot how to do it.

BAT. Shall I teach you again?

POPPI. No. All their feathers were ruffled. Teach me another.

BAT. Would you like to make a little cloud come sailing in through the window, and rain all over the room?

POPPI. Umm . . . oh, but it would be wet, wouldn't it?

BAT. You're too particular for real sorcery. I'll make all the eggs go bad. Listen.

POPPI [*staring at him, fascinated*]. Yis?

BAT.   Feathers black and feathers blue,
          All the eggs go bad . . . pfooo!

[*There is a furious clucking from the basket by the fire.*]

[25]

POPPI. Oh, you've turned Broodie's clutch of eggs bad. You are naughty, Bat!

BAT. You asked me to.

POPPI. I never! I didn't mean really do it. Poor old Broodie. Poor, poor chicken, and she's been sitting so patient.

BAT. I'll take her mind, and herself, off her eggs.

       Eeeny, meeny, miney, mo,
       Uppy, chicky, up go!

[*The unfortunate hen rises out of the basket with a squawk, and then sinks slowly down again.*]

POPPI. Oh, Broodie! There, Broodie . . . there, hen.

[*He soothes the hen, and settles her on her basket again.* BAT *wanders away, bored.*]

BAT. Hens are stupid things, like you.

POPPI. Hens are nice. She hated being lifted like that by magic. She's cross, now.

BAT. Let's not disturb ourselves for the emotions of a hen. I might have turned her green.

POPPI. You're not to. Poor chicky is all ruffled, already.

BAT. Well, what do you want to learn? I can teach you to make a thunder-storm. To leash the lightning. To make the trees toss their branches, without a wind. To turn honeysuckle into deadly nightshade.

POPPI [*staring*]. Yis?

BAT. I can show you how to slide on a patch of moonlight as though it were ice. To wear a live snake, asleep, for a belt . . .

POPPI. No, Bat. I don't like your snake. I wish you'd take it off.

BAT. That I cannot do. But it does no harm, and is beautiful, like an embroidery of jewels.

POPPI. Well, it's horrid as a belt.

BAT. It is the badge that all my father's servants wear.

POPPI. You're not his servant.

BAT [*moving away, arrogantly*]. I am his son.

POPPI. Oh . . . come back, Bat! Tell me some more about magic. Not big, black, noisy spells like thunder and snakes. But little, cosy magic . . . just here, together, in the room.

BAT. Very well, stupid. I'll make the hens sing.

POPPI. Can they sing?

BAT. I can make them.

> Sleepy hens, stupid things,
> Feathery heads under feathery wings,
> Hear my magic, right or wrong,
> Sing a stupid feathery song.
> [*A small chorus of gentle, hen-like voices begins to croon;*

HENS' SONG. We'll croon
> Under the moon,
> To a sleepy, stupid tune;
> Rock to and fro,
> Never crow,
> Hens can only croon, you know.
> Eggs and feathers and beaks and toes
> Are all we think as we sit in rows
> And croon, croon,
> Sleepy under the moon;
> Crooooooon . . .

BAT. Oh stop! That's enough! I almost went to sleep myself.

POPPI. I think I *did*.

BAT. I'll wake us up. You watch this!

POPPI. Do be careful, Bat. You always do something awful when you look like that.

BAT.	Blow wind, thunder roar,
	Storm rouse, rain pour!
	Demons of the tempest loud,
	Ride the lightning from the cloud!

[*As he shouts the words, wind and thunder begin to rise outside the cottage, with a flicker of lightning.*]

POPPI. Oh, don't! You mustn't! Bat . . . Bat, the Henwife said you were not to make magic when she was not here. She said that it might bring . . . him!

BAT. It is my storm and I am master of it!

[*The storm mounts, and through it can be heard heavy thuds, like terrible footsteps approaching nearer, outside the window.*]

POPPI. Listen, oh, listen! I can hear footsteps in the thunder!

BAT [*afraid*]. No! It is my storm . . . not his!

[*The footsteps are very loud now, and also the wind and thunder. The lightning gives a great flash, and* HEMLOCK *is in the room.*]

HEMLOCK. Your storms are easily mastered, my son.

[HEMLOCK *is tall and terrible, with a crown of snakes, and a green-shadowed, implacable face. The cold eyes glitter like emeralds, and even the long hair is green on his shoulders. Magic jewels glow on his fine hands, and over his huge trailing cloak.* BAT *moves away from him to the opposite wall, but* POPPI *sits centre, staring fascinated with his mouth open.*]

Bat, I have come for you.

BAT. I . . . but I . . . No!

[28]

HEMLOCK. Has so brief a sojourn in this uncouth hut cost you the use of your tongue?

BAT. I wish to . . . to stay here, sir.

HEMLOCK. You are mad to say so. Shall I permit my son to become servant to a hag who keeps hens!

POPPI. He's not a servant, and she isn't a hag. Nice, she is . . . nice.

HEMLOCK. What is this? The Salamander? The little pet of the forest . . . pretty thing!

POPPI [*pleased*]. You think I'm pretty? Oh, how kind.

> [*He fawns on* HEMLOCK, *who sneers and draws away from him.*]

HEMLOCK. Listen, creature. Would you like a present?

POPPI. Yis. I would indeed.

HEMLOCK. Something beautiful. Bright and shining, and desired by all.

BAT [*understanding*]. No! Poppi!

HEMLOCK. Hold your tongue! Look . . . er . . . Poppi, would you like these gleaming toys?

> [*He holds up two large golden coins.* POPPI *is delighted.*]

POPPI. Yis . . . pretty, oh pretty! Thank you, you're not bad and wicked, at all. You're very, very nice.

BAT. You mustn't take them.

POPPI. Not?

BAT. The Henwife said . . .

HEMLOCK. She never forbade little Poppi to take a pretty gift, did she?

POPPI. No, indeed, she never did.

> [BAT *covers his face in dismay.* POPPI *frisks round* HEMLOCK.]

Thank you, thank you, thank you, thank you . . .

HEMLOCK. Stop running round and round! I'm quite giddy. Come, *dear*, and take your toys.

[POPPI *extends his paws, happily, but* HEMLOCK *withholds the coins, teasingly, above his head.*]

Before I give you these, you must thank me. . . .

POPPI. Thank you . . . thank you . . . thank you . . .

HEMLOCK. That's enough! In the words I bid you use. Listen.

POPPI. What do I have to say?

HEMLOCK. I accept the two gold coins in exchange for your son.

POPPI. Yis. I accept the two . . . are those coins? I thought they were toys.

HEMLOCK. Same thing! Go on.

POPPI. Yis . . . the two gold coins . . . in exchange . . . what?

HEMLOCK. In exchange for your son.

POPPI. Now I've forgotten the beginning.

HEMLOCK [*seething*]. I accept the two gold . . .

POPPI. Fancy those being coins.

HEMLOCK [*shouting*]. Say the words, you little fool!

POPPI. Yis, oh yis! [*Pause.*] What *were* the words?

HEMLOCK. Stupid, brainless thing!

[*He throws* POPPI *on the ground, and puts a foot on him.*]

POPPI. Ow! Ow! I'm squashing!

HEMLOCK. Say the words I told you to say.

POPPI [*wailing*]. I've forgotten . . .

HEMLOCK. I'll repeat them. Just once again. If you do not say them this time, I shall really squash you.

POPPI. You're not nice! You're horrid! I would have said the words, if you'd given me time. Now, I'll never remember.

HEMLOCK. You must. Listen. I accept the two gold coins . . .

POPPI. I'm getting angry. I'm getting hot.

HEMLOCK. Will you listen!

BAT. No, Poppi. You must not say the words, or take the coins . . . Whatever threats he may use——

HEMLOCK. Wait till I get you to the castle, boy!

POPPI. I'm sizzling!

HEMLOCK. I'm burnt!

[*He springs away from* POPPI, *and* BAT *backs quickly to left.*]

POPPI. I'm red-hot! I'm that cross, now, I'm all afire.

[*And indeed his short tail is now glowing red.*]

HEMLOCK. Keep away from me!

POPPI. I'll not take your horrid present and I won't say any of the words you tell me! I'll do nothing for you, but burn you, you nasty, nasty person!

HEMLOCK. Bat, this delay will add to your reckoning. I shall come for you again.

POPPI. Go away! Go away, at once!

HEMLOCK. Indeed, I shall. And when I return, I will regain my son, if I have to use every power of my sorcery to do so.

[*There is a flash of lightning, a roar of wind and thunder, and the* SORCERER *is gone. The thudding of his footsteps dies away in the night outside.*]

POPPI. I think I'd better cool down, or I shall set the room on fire. Bat . . . Bat, it's all right. He's gone. You taught me a spell once to make the fire die down. Tell me again, so that I can make me cool.

BAT [*dully*]. I have forgotten it.

POPPI. Oh, have you, Bat? You? I thought it was only me who forgot things.

[BAT *sighs once, and tries to pull himself together. He is considerably shaken, and sobered.*]

BAT. It's usually you.

POPPI. Tell me the words to make a fire die down. I'm still sizzling a bit. Go on. Do.

BAT. It's quite simple.

[*He waves a hand.*]

Round about,
Fire out.

POPPI. I'm still pretty warm. Your spell wasn't much use.

BAT. Few spells are much use against living creatures. That is, if they are . . .

[*He pauses, uncertainly.*]

POPPI. Are what?

BAT. Creatures that you like.

POPPI. Do you mean you like me? Oh, Bat, do you? Do you?

BAT. Do I? I . . . cannot tell.

POPPI. *Now* I'm cool again. Nice, nice Bat.

BAT. I said, I cannot tell. Go away. Look, that fire's out.

POPPI. Oh. Whatever will the Henwife . . .?

BAT. Get hot again, and sit on it.

POPPI. I have to get really furious before I'm hot enough to make it light that way. I could do my fire-spell, but the porridge would get ruined in the hotness of it.

BAT [*crossing to look*]. It looks odd, anyway. It's all this magic . . . it's turned the porridge. Let's go away, before the Henwife finds out.

[32]

POPPI. No, we mustn't. She told us to stay here, **Bat**.

BAT. I started the magic, and I will be blamed. I cannot stand any more, just now! I must get away.

> [*He goes to the door.* POPPI *runs after, and tries to stop him.*]

POPPI. Where are you going? Not out there, Bat. There was a reason . . . I've forgotten it, but there was a reason!

BAT. Let go of me. I shall go into the forest, and hide there until the Henwife is too anxious to be angry.

POPPI. How horrid of you to upset her!

> [*But* BAT *evades him, and goes out quickly.*]

Come back here! Oh, I mustn't let him go out in the dark alone. Wait for me, Bat! I can run faster than you, anyway . . .

> [*He runs out after* BAT. *The hens cluck, worriedly. The* HENWIFE *calls, offstage right.*]

HENWIFE [*off*]. Briony, are you home, dear?

> [*The hens go on clucking. After a moment the* HENWIFE *enters.*]

Where are you all? Poppi! Bat! Are you all hiding? Is this a game, my dears? Oh, do answer, I'm so anxious.

> [*She looks round the room. The hens cluck.*]

The room is full of magic. What has happened here, since I went out? Magic . . . magic . . . who has been making magic here? Grey magic. Small grey magic. That would be Bat . . . naughty boy, he is always making grey magic. Oh but . . . yes, I can smell black magic, too! That is terrible. What has happened? Bat! [*She puts her hand to her head.*] I only have one really big spell, and I've been saving it for an emergency. Is this the moment? Broodie, dear, tell

[33]

me . . . what has become of Briony, and Bat, and little Poppi? Tell me.

[*The hen in the basket clucks, and croons.*]

Wait and see? Is that all you can say? Oh, how difficult. I don't like the smell of magic in this cottage. Black magic, and grey magic . . . how horrid! And the fire is quite out. And the porridge . . .?

[*She lifts the lid, and bubbles fly out.*]

Mercy me, the porridge has turned to soap-suds!

CURTAIN

UNDER A TREE IN THE FOREST

The tree is rather a peculiar one in many ways, and REYNARD *stands looking up into its branches with some misgivings.*

REYNARD. This looks like the tree the Baron mentioned, don't you think, Rufus?

(*Ru.*) No, I don't.

He said that the trunk went round in spirals, and the leaves were blue and mauve.

(*Ru.*) He said nothing about that dead branch.

Maybe he didn't notice the dead branch, Rufus.

(*Ru.*) It's fairly conspicuous.

It isn't.

(*Ru.*) It is! Shut up, do, or I'll kick you!

You can't possibly.

(*Ru.*) I can, too.

> [*He indulges in a series of strange contortions, with
> the result that he finally hacks himself on the ankle,
> and howls aloud.*]

Now look what you've done!

(*Ru.*) I can feel what I've done. It's me I've kicked,
too.

(*Ru.*) Let's sit down, shall we?

> [*The suggestion is accepted. While the ankle is being
> tenderly massaged, the* BARON *enters.*]

WILLIAM. Where are you?

REYNARD. We're here, sir.

WILLIAM. What are you sitting there for?

REYNARD. We kicked us on the ankle, sir, and we're
just rubbing it.

WILLIAM. Reynard, you're out of your mind.

REYNARD. Minds. And really I think you should call
us Runard.

WILLIAM. I'll call you worse than that, if you don't
stand up and stop playing the fool.

REYNARD. Fools.

> [REYNARD *scrambles to his feet . . . no, we'll call
> him Runard, as he suggested.* RUNARD *scrambles
> to his feet.*]

WILLIAM. It was here I last saw Finian, sitting on that
branch.

RUNARD. The dead one?

WILLIAM. No . . . yes, that one. But it was not dead
last time. The falcon had some of the leaves caught
up in his claws. He must have flown again, startled
by something, maybe. He won't fly far in the dark,
though. He'll want to perch and sleep.

[36]

RUNARD. Like us.

WILLIAM. You'll not sleep till the falcon's found. Search in the near-by trees. I'll go this way, and you that. If you see him perching, come quietly and call me. Make no move that will rouse him. Understand, gaby?

RUNARD. I think so, my lord.

WILLIAM. I wish Rufus was here.

RUNARD. (*Ru.*) I am here, sir. I understand. And Finian knows me well.

WILLIAM. More than I do. Anyway, make no attempt to catch him yourself. I wouldn't trust you to catch at a straw.

[*He goes out, to the right.*]

RUNARD. Why would I want to catch at a straw?

(*Ru.*) Come along, Reynard. This way.

It's dark through there. I don't like it.

(*Ru.*) The Baron said . . .

I don't care what he said. He likes this sort of thing, but I want to go home.

(*Ru.*) Reynard, pull ourselves together, will you.

[RUNARD *moves off towards the right, but starts hanging back.*]

What's that? Something coming through the shadows. Oh, let's run away! Let's call the Baron! Rufus . . .

(*Ru.*) Shut up, do. Who's there?

Oooooh!

POPPI [*offstage*]. Me! Us!

RUNARD. (*Ru.*) Is that Poppi?

[POPPI *comes frisking on, followed silently and watchfully by* BAT, *who leans against a tree.*]

(*Ru.*) Did you find Briony?

[37]

POPPI. No, Briony's lost. This is Bat. Nice Bat.

RUNARD. Nice? He looks an odd sort of nice to me.

POPPI. His father's a sorcerer, that's why he's a little unusual.

RUNARD. Ye . . . es, that could be it.

(*Ru.*) If Briony's lost, oughtn't we to look for her?

POPPI. Mother Henwife's looking.

BAT. And you yourself are lost, are you not?

RUNARD. I don't care for that remark. What are you laughing at anyway?

BAT. You. To talk of searching for Briony, in this forest, under this moon . . . and you a mere human in any case.

RUNARD. We don't want to speak to you, and we'd prefer you to go right away.

POPPI. But . . . Bat's nice, you know. You might not think so, sometimes, but he is.

RUNARD. We *don't* think so. You just take your friend home, will you.

BAT. I will decide what I do.

RUNARD. (*Ru.*) You'd better both cut along before the Baron comes back. You, Poppi, you don't want another arrow after you, do you?

POPPI. Oooh, is that man here? He pushed me.

RUNARD. (*Ru.*) He would have done more than that.

POPPI. Bat, do come. I mustn't leave you, and that rough man might come and push me again.

BAT. Perhaps he would like to try pushing me.

RUNARD. I'd help him.

BAT. I know a spell that would make you take root in the ground. Leaves would spring from your hands,

[38]

and your hair would rise and thicken into branches. And the strange creatures of the forest would build nests on your shoulders. Shall I try?

RUNARD [*backing away*]. No! How dare you! I'll scream. I'll fetch the Baron, and he'll hunt you, too. You're nothing but a nasty sorcerer, and fit quarry for a right-thinking hunter.

BAT. Neither you or your Baron could do much hunting, if you were just a couple of rather dowdy trees.

RUNARD. You need a good smacking, you do.

BAT. Would you like to try?

RUNARD. Not half. But I won't tonight. You go away, that's all. I wish someone would come. Rufus, call the Baron! I think everyone in this forest is hateful, I do.

BAT. You're afraid of everyone.

RUNARD. Don't you come near me, you beastly boy! If your father's anything of a sorcerer, why doesn't he keep you in order?

POPPI. He would, if he could. He wants, more than anything, to catch Bat, and take him back to the castle up there, in the mists.

RUNARD. Well, I wish him luck. I'd like Bat to be up there in the mists, and the mistier the better. I wish his father would come and take him away, now, this minute!

POPPI. You shouldn't say that. Listen!

[*There is a groan of thunder, and a rising wind, and the thud of the* SORCERER's *footsteps approaching.*]

RUNARD. What's that dreadful thumping noise?

BAT. He is coming! Run quickly . . .

RUNARD. Here, don't leave me! Come back!

D   [39]

[BAT *tries to run, but* RUNARD *seizes him for support, shaking with fright. The* SORCERER *enters.*]

HEMLOCK. Someone spoke of me. Did you call me, Bat?

BAT. No.

HEMLOCK. Your manners are still deplorable. And what company are you keeping this time? I had news of strangers here tonight. I meant to attend to them, if the forest itself did not destroy them. Why are you gaping so? Do you not care for moonlight?

RUNARD. It was better before you came.

HEMLOCK. I will cheer you with a gift.

RUNARD [*suspiciously*]. What sort of gift?

POPPI. Nice?

BAT. No!

HEMLOCK. Some think it nicer than anything.

RUNARD. And no turnings-into-trees, like that horrid boy said?

HEMLOCK. Did he suggest that? He was showing off, I fear. My son is not yet an experienced sorcerer.

RUNARD. Yes, you take him away, and learn him.

HEMLOCK. Would you like these two gold coins?

RUNARD. Oh, rather!

POPPI. What are they?

HEMLOCK. You wouldn't remember. [*To* RUNARD.] Will you sell my son to me, for these coins?

RUNARD. How can I? He isn't mine.

HEMLOCK. It's merely a form of speech. All you must do is to accept the coins from me, and say . . .

POPPI. Are those coins?

HEMLOCK. Lie down!

RUNARD. And say what, sir?

HEMLOCK. I accept the two gold coins in exchange for your son.

RUNARD. Oh, well, that's simple enough. I don't mind just a form of speech. I accept the two gold . . . well, what about it? Let's have 'em, eh?

BAT. Don't touch them! I implore you not to touch them!

RUNARD. You let go of my sleeve, young man. You and your sprouting trees!

HEMLOCK. I am waiting. Here are the coins.

RUNARD. Well—thanks. [*He takes them.*]

BAT. Throw them away. They're bad.

RUNARD [*biting one*]. They're gold.

HEMLOCK. Now for the form of speech.

RUNARD. Oh, yes. What was it?

HEMLOCK [*suppressing his ire*]. I accept the two gold . . .

POPPI [*helpfully*]. Coins.

HEMLOCK. Thank you, *dear*! In exchange for your son.

RUNARD. I've got it. *And* the money. So here goes. I accept the two gold coins, with thanks, in exchange for your son. And a bargain at the price.

> [*A pause.* BAT *crosses stiffly to the* SORCERER'S *side.* HEMLOCK *touches him on the shoulder, and he lowers his head and stays very still.*]

RUNARD. You can have Poppi for sixpence.

HEMLOCK. What do you say!

RUNARD. (*Ru.*) Reynard, are you mad? Poppi?

POPPI. Poppi?

RUNARD. Yes, what do I care! I'm fed up with this forest, and I'm going home. Anyone can have anybody in it for anything they like to pay.

HEMLOCK. I accept your offer.

[41]

POPPI [*almost in tears*]. But I'm Briony's Poppi, I am.

HEMLOCK. Then come with me to Briony. She is in my hunting-lodge, now. Here, take your sixpence.

RUNARD. (*Ru.*) No, Reynard, stop it!
Shan't. I accept the sixpence in exchange for Poppi. There!

> [*He takes the sixpence.*]

HEMLOCK. Come here, Poppi *dear*!

> [POPPI *walks stiffly across to the* SORCERER. HEMLOCK *touches him on the shoulder, and he sinks down to lie at his feet.*]

HEMLOCK. My thanks, huntsman. I will allow you to escape from the forest with your life and sanity . . . such as it is. But only on condition that you go now. At once. If you linger here till the moon is at its height, you shall stay here for ever.

RUNARD. Oh, we'll go now.

> [*At this moment* WILLIAM *enters, right.*]

WILLIAM. *Now* what is going on?

HEMLOCK. Your man is about to leave the forest, and if you are wise you will go too.

WILLIAM. Thank you for your advice, but I'll stay till I have found my falcon. Reynard, where . . .?

HEMLOCK. Your falcon?

WILLIAM. Finian flew into this tree, sir.

HEMLOCK. Yes. And his name is Finian? A splendid bird.

WILLIAM. Have you seen him?

HEMLOCK. A great sorcerer sees most things.

WILLIAM. You're jesting. Magic is nothing but non-sense.

HEMLOCK. Indeed? Yet the branch of that tree was

[42]

killed when my magic brought Finian captive to my hand.

WILLIAM. You . . . took my falcon?

RUNARD. Be careful, my lord. This is no place to bandy words with a sorcerer.

WILLIAM. Sorcerer? He's nothing but a poacher.

RUNARD. No, my lord! Stop! He'll do something awful to you. To all of us! To *me*!

[HEMLOCK *has raised his hands, and does indeed look awful.*]

WILLIAM. I absolutely defy him to do anything at all.

RUNARD [*to* HEMLOCK, *in a panic*]. Oh . . . mercy, sir . . . forgive him! Don't start any magic . . . I believe in it! Look, you can take him, if you'll let me go. I'll sell you the Baron for nothing.

HEMLOCK. Do you mean that!

RUNARD [*babbling*]. I accept nothing at all in exchange for the Baron. You can have him for the taking.

[*A pause. The* BARON *stands still, looking puzzled and a bit dazed, his eyes on the* SORCERER.]

RUNARD. (*Ru.*) Reynard, what have you done?

HEMLOCK. Come here.

WILLIAM. No.

HEMLOCK. So you are stronger than the others, and will try to resist? You will find that I am stronger still.

[*He crosses to* WILLIAM, *and touches him on the shoulder, and the* BARON *lowers his head.* HEMLOCK *turns to* RUNARD.]

I am grateful to you for giving me possession of these three. They shall come with me now to my hunting-lodge. There are other prisoners there already,

[43]

awaiting my return. And then they shall be taken to my great castle, and there will be sorcery there in plenty before the dawn.

RUNARD [*indicating the* BARON, *sheepishly*]. What . . . are you going to do with him?

HEMLOCK. You spoke of tree-spells. There are worse things to which one can be transformed than a tree. Far worse. Ask no more. But if ever you should happen to look on this handsome noble again—be sure you will not recognize him!

[*He goes out, with a hand on the* BARON'S *shoulder.* BAT *follows, with* POPPI *clinging to his sleeve. The thud of* HEMLOCK'S *footsteps dies away in the distance.*]

RUNARD. (*Ru.*) Reynard! You rotten coward! To sell the Baron . . . !

He would have got us all transformed, the way he was carrying on.

(*Ru.*) What are we now?

Well, don't think I want to be stuck to you for the rest of my life, my dear Rufus. But I do *want* a rest to my life, so I'm off now.

(*Ru.*) You're not.

I am.

(*Ru.*) Not!

Am.

[*The* HENWIFE *enters.*]

Oh!

HENWIFE [*breathlessly*]. Have you seen my daughter? Or a boy named Bat? Have you met Poppi? Oh, for mercy's sake, stop goggling, and answer.

RUNARD. Er . . . yes . . . no . . . some of them.

HENWIFE. Where?

RUNARD. Around and about.

HENWIFE. Oh, I'm distracted. Where are they!

RUNARD. I don't know, and I don't care. I'm off.

(*Ru.*) Reynard, you must stay here to help the Baron, and the others.

Me? No fear!

[*He tries to run away, but catches himself by the back of the neck and drags himself back.*]

HENWIFE. Is this the moment for a romp!

RUNARD. I'll bite you, Rufus, so I will. Ow! Ow!

(*Ru.*) You spiteful thing!

[*He has bitten himself in the arm, and wails.*]

HENWIFE [*amazed*]. Why, the man's bewitched.

RUNARD. Yes, I am indeed, and it's awful. Oooh!

(*Ru.*) Take a grip on ourselves, Reynard.

HENWIFE. Yes, do.

RUNARD. I can't take a grip on anything. Our hands are shaking so.

HENWIFE. You come with me to my hut, and tell me all about it. It's quite obvious you're under a very lamentable enchantment. I can protect you, if you will stay indoors.

RUNARD. Both of us?

HENWIFE. Er . . . yes, possibly.

RUNARD. (*Ru.*) We'll come, mistress. We've things to tell you that you should know. Though you may not find them happy hearing.

Yes, let's get out of here. Quick! Look at that tree . . . it's turning greener and greener!

(*Ru.*) All right, don't panic.

HENWIFE. Stop muttering, and come with me . . . both of you.

[RUNARD *pulls one of his hands over towards the* HENWIFE, *who seizes it and goes off with him, hurriedly. The light in the glade has changed, and the tree has a weird light of its own. An owl hoots eerily from the shadows.*]

CURTAIN

THE SORCERER'S HUNTING-LODGE

HEMLOCK *has made his hunting-lodge out of an unpleasant cave half-way up the mountain. The rough arch of a low doorway at the back is heavily barred. Down right, there is a dark opening in the rock that leads to another part of the cave. And there is a fireplace left. The only furniture consists of a wooden table, and a chair. Near the doorway at the back is a perch, with a falcon crouched on it, a chain round his leg.* BRIONY *is stroking his feathers, looking nervously round her.*

BRIONY. Poor falcon, poor bird . . . how you long to fly away. This cave frightens you, my dear, and oh, how it frightens me! I have often heard talk of the Sorcerer's hunting-lodge, half-way up to the castle

on the top of the mountain. Here he brings his poor
captives from the forest, and when he has taken them
from this place to the castle . . . there, who can tell
what happens to them? Restless bird, you are
throbbing with fear. How you hate the chain on your
leg. I would loose you if I could . . . but I am a
prisoner, too. Those bars hold me, as helpless as
you. Don't look at me, falcon . . . turn your eyes
away . . . I can do nothing.

> [*She goes to the barred archway, and looks out into the
> dark.*]

The doorway into the forest is barred, and fastened
with spells. And will not open until the Sorcerer
returns.

> [*She runs back to the fireplace, and covers her face.*]

What will he do with me? Surely he'll not harm me,
for my mother holds his son . . . oh, but he knows she
will never hurt Bat. Who is coming . . . there's someone coming . . . oh, not yet! Not yet!

> [*The sound of the* SORCERER'S *footsteps can be
> heard. Then the barred door opens, and* HEMLOCK
> *enters with* WILLIAM. *He leads the* BARON *to the
> wall at the back, and fastens him by the wrists to
> two chains attached there.* WILLIAM *moves stiffly,
> as though invisibly compelled.*]

HEMLOCK [*to* BRIONY]. Have you been lonely? Here
is company for you. You . . . [*to* WILLIAM] . . .
what is your name?

WILLIAM. That is my affair.

HEMLOCK. You will answer more humbly soon.

> [*He goes to the doorway, and looks out.*]

Bat! Why are you skulking in the dark? Do you
think I shall forget you?

[BAT *comes in, with* POPPI. HEMLOCK *catches his son by the shoulder in the doorway, and* POPPI *creeps under the table.*]

Be rid of any idea that you can escape again.

[BAT *has seen* BRIONY, *and he looks at her nervously.*]

BAT. Why is she here?

HEMLOCK. Do you dare question me?

BAT. What are you going to do with her?

HEMLOCK. Occupy your fears for yourself, boy.

WILLIAM. Perhaps you'll answer *me*. Why is the girl here?

HEMLOCK. You, too, should rather be concerned with your own fate. I had hoped better from you. For you have little heart that I can discern—and possibly, with tuition, you may——

WILLIAM. Never mind about my heart! What about answering my question?

HEMLOCK. The girl? She is to be my kitchenmaid.

BRIONY. Forever?

HEMLOCK. Do you think I should return you to your hag-mother in thanks for her care of my son?

BAT. She was kind to me, and kept me safe.

HEMLOCK. I shall keep her daughter safe.

POPPI. And the Henwife isn't a hag!

HEMLOCK. Where is that creature?

[*He drags* POPPI *out, resisting, from under the table.*]

I had almost forgotten about you.

POPPI. Leave me alone . . . no! I won't come! No!

HEMLOCK. You'll stay here, on a collar and chain, like a tame dog, until I decide what to do with you.

[HEMLOCK *drags him over to the fireplace, and puts a collar and chain on him. There is a large dog-basket on the hearth, and* POPPI *climbs into this, and sits in it.*]

POPPI. Nasty! Nasty! Grrrrr . . .

HEMLOCK [*with a slap*]. Down!

POPPI. You look out, or I'll sizzle!

HEMLOCK. If you dare . . .

BRIONY. No, Poppi, be careful, darling! Sit still. You can do no good by sizzling. Not just now.

[POPPI *glares at* HEMLOCK *for a moment, then subsides in the basket, his chin on his front paws.*]

POPPI. All right. Later.

WILLIAM [*to* HEMLOCK]. Must you bully a girl and a small animal?

HEMLOCK. Must you hunt?

WILLIAM. Where's the connection?

HEMLOCK. Obviously, it is always amusing to create fear. We are both hunters, young man, though on this occasion you have found yourself in the unpleasant position of being the quarry. We enjoy the humiliation of the terrified creatures, as they run, and twist, and cower.

WILLIAM. Nonsense. I hunt for sport.

HEMLOCK. That's what I was saying. Bat, go and bring me food. You remember the simple magic necessary? Or do I have to remind you?

[*He looks menacing, and* BAT *moves quickly to the archway, right.*]

BAT. No. I remember.

[*He goes out.*]

HEMLOCK. He will soon come back to heel. I have been too lenient in the past.

[50]

BRIONY. Lenient? He ran away because he was afraid of you. He hated your sorcery and your hunting . . .

HEMLOCK. Are you telling me that he is slightly human?

POPPI. Yis, he said he thought he liked me.

HEMLOCK. Did he indeed? That is a dangerous sign—and I must deal with it.

WILLIAM. I have never heard such talk of magic! Sorcery! Spells! All moonshine!

HEMLOCK. You think so?

WILLIAM. It isn't reasonable to think anything else. Magic is nothing but tales for children.

HEMLOCK. Not my sort of magic.

WILLIAM. Tell that to young girls . . . Briony may believe you . . . or to animals like . . .

HEMLOCK. Like what? Is Poppi such an ordinary animal? Is there no magic about him?

WILLIAM. Well . . . he's . . . they said there were strange animals in the forest. And even a talking red puppy need not be a matter of enchantment.

POPPI. Not?

WILLIAM. Not.

HEMLOCK. You'll learn sense, young man. . . . What did you say your name was?

WILLIAM. Find out!

HEMLOCK. Certainly.

[BAT *comes in, carrying a tray with a roasted pea-cock, also a large egg in a golden, jewelled cup. He puts these on the table, with some golden plates, and knives, etc. A flagon and a glass.*]

You took your time, boy.

BAT. I forgot the words for a cockatrice's egg.

HEMLOCK. You forget too much.

POPPI. Wish I had some food. I'm hungry.

HEMLOCK. Then watch me eat.

> [*He sits at the table, and* BAT *pours him some wine.
> The* SORCERER *looks round the cave, and then at*
> WILLIAM.]

Did you notice the falcon, young man?

WILLIAM. I saw my falcon when I came in.

HEMLOCK. He *was* your falcon. Soon he will belong
to no one.

BRIONY. Don't hurt the bird. How can you!

HEMLOCK. I will have silence here, while I enjoy my
meal.

POPPI. Feathers black and feathers blue,
     All the eggs go bad . . . pfooo!

> [*The egg which the* SORCERER *is about to eat
> goes green.* BAT *laughs unexpectedly, and* HEM-
> LOCK *glares at him. He stops laughing im-
> mediately.*]

HEMLOCK. I'll deal with you, my son, later.
     Magic egg of cockatrice,
     Instantly again be nice.

> [*The egg goes white again.* POPPI *jumps up and
> down.*]

POPPI. Feathers black and feathers blue,
     All the eggs go bad . . . pfooo!

> [*The egg turns green, and the* SORCERER *rises.*]

HEMLOCK. Lie down! Be silent!

POPPI [*greatly excited*]. Nasty! Nasty! Shan't eat his
supper! Pfooo!

WILLIAM. Good old Poppi!

POPPI. Good old Poppi! Pfooo!

HEMLOCK. Take this away, Bat, at once! Do you
hear?

[52]

BAT. What?

> [*The* SORCERER *thrusts the egg into his hands,*
> *furiously.*]

Oh, yes. Yes, sir.

> [BAT *places the egg at the other side of the table.*
> HEMLOCK *glares at him, and then round at the*
> *others, then sets his knife to the roasted peacock.*]

POPPI.   Eeny, meeny, miney, mo,
            Uppy, chicky, up go!

> [*The peacock rises into the air, and away up out of*
> *sight.* HEMLOCK *stares after it in amazement.*
> WILLIAM *is puzzled, as he does not believe in*
> *spells.* BAT *gives his sudden irrepressible laugh,*
> *and the* SORCERER *rises, and glares down at him,*
> *so that he stops suddenly.*]

HEMLOCK. Twice you have laughed—at me!

> [*He puts a hand on* BAT'S *wrist.*]

BAT. It was a mistake.

> [*He lowers his head.*]

HEMLOCK. Be sure of that.

BRIONY. You're hurting him!

WILLIAM.   Loose these chains, and turn your boasted
spells against me if you're so sure of your magic.
Try whether I am as easily cowed by a word!

HEMLOCK. Your turn will come. [*He looks at* BAT.
A pause. BAT *tries to speak, but fails.*]
You would like to ally yourself with these three . . .
against me. You think they are your friends? Very
well. I shall put a spell over them, now, all three
. . . a very little spell . . . oh, quite a minor spell . . .
and you shall see how much their friendship is worth.
How long it will last, against a petty spell.

WILLIAM. Another spell!

HEMLOCK. Just a small one, to teach my too impulsive son a lesson.

BRIONY. What will happen?

WILLIAM [*to her*]. Don't be afraid, Briony.

> [*She goes close to him, and stares wide-eyed at* HEMLOCK, *feeling some sort of safety beside* WILLIAM'S *practicality, however limited he may be in action.*]

HEMLOCK. I throw a web of cobweb over the whole cave.

> [*He waves his hands slowly, and the place darkens.*]

In every tendril of darkness, pulsates the power of black sorcery.

> [*The gloom of the cave is suddenly shot through with flickers of green, and the* SORCERER *lifts his arms high.*]

> > Gentleness shall now abate,
> > Kindly feeling turn to hate,
> > Friendliness to scorn and fear
> > While the spell shall domineer;
> > Turn against my son, and prove
> > Little value lies in love.

BRIONY. Unfair! You're using magic. But I'll never turn against Bat . . . never . . .

> [*She stiffens suddenly, and her face goes cold and rigid. She turns and looks at* BAT *with distaste, and moves farther away from him.*]

HEMLOCK. You *have* turned against him. So have the others. Now he will find out the value of doing without feelings. I'll eat in peace, elsewhere. He'll be glad enough to come to me, when he finds how you three will deal with him. Then I shall take you all to my castle, and there begin the great sorceries of

[54]

full moon and midnight. Make the most of the short time left.

> [*He goes out through the archway, right.* WILLIAM *tugs at his chains.*]

WILLIAM. Spells! If I could get my hands free, I'd twist his head off for him!

BRIONY. Don't tug so. You'll hurt yourself.

WILLIAM. Is there nothing that might break these links? Is there a knife on the table . . . the chain is light.

BAT. The iron is forged from thunder-bolts.

WILLIAM. There's no call for you to make stupid comments.

BAT. It was not particularly stupid. Nothing could break those links.

BRIONY. How pleased you sound.

WILLIAM. He's jeering at my helplessness.

> [*When they speak to* BAT, *or of him, their voices become hard and unlike the friendlier tones they used before.*]

BAT. Briony, you said you wouldn't turn against me . . . even for magic.

BRIONY. What do you mean?

WILLIAM. All this talk of magic is quite unhinging. Go away.

BRIONY. Leave us alone.

WILLIAM. Give me that knife on the table, Briony.

BAT. It would turn to a snake in your hand. This place is full of my father's magic.

WILLIAM. Am I afraid of your father? Do you think me as craven as yourself?

BRIONY. Even *he* couldn't suppose that!

WILLIAM. Who knows the working of an inhuman mind?

E   [55]

BAT. Briony—[*She turns away.*] How stupid you are! Don't you realize what has happened to you? Poppi, is the spell on your warm heart, also?

[POPPI *growls, and tries to bite his hand.*]

Oh, not you, too!

POPPI. If you touch me, I'll burn you.

BAT. You wouldn't!

POPPI. I'm getting hotter and hotter while I speak.

[*He strains at his collar and chain, to bite at* BAT, *and coughs.*]

I'll bite, I will! I will! I'm cross, and it's making me cough, 'cos the collar's so tight . . .

BAT. You've got it twisted.

BRIONY. Don't you dare touch my Poppi!

POPPI. Or I'll start sizzling.

BAT. I was only going to straighten your collar. Poppi, listen to me . . . those two are under a spell that makes them hate me. . . .

WILLIAM. Stop talking nonsense about spells, do!

BAT. But you have kind feelings for me still.

POPPI [*uncertainly*]. Yis . . . no . . . maybe . . .

BRIONY. Don't speak to him, Poppi. Mother Henwife wouldn't wish you to.

BAT. She would! She would! She always told me to be kind to you, because you were so loving.

POPPI [*doubtfully*]. Yis, I was very loving.

BRIONY. And were you kind? Ever? No. Always bad and heartless. You know it. You teased and tormented Poppi, because he was little. And if he did love you once, he's learned better now.

BAT. Do you really hate me? All of you?

WILLIAM. Does that surprise you so?

BAT. Even Poppi?

BRIONY [*to* POPPI]. Don't answer him.

POPPI. I'll burn his fingers if he comes near me, shall I?

BAT. A little, minor piece of magic, and this is all your friendship was worth!

POPPI. I am friends, Bat. I mean, I *was* friends. . . .

BAT. I didn't think this could happen—even by sorcery. Nor did I know how much I valued friendship—until now, when I see how little it can be trusted.

WILLIAM. Even your name is grotesque.

BAT. What is wrong with it?

WILLIAM. Who gave you such a name?

BAT [*almost in tears at such harrying*]. My godmother.

WILLIAM. And what sort of creature was she?

BAT. She was a bat.

WILLIAM [*laughs*]. How very suitable.

BRIONY. He's not human. He's a witch-boy.

BAT. Poppi . . .

POPPI. Go away, or I'll sizzle!

BRIONY. Don't you hurt Poppi.

BAT. Do you think I would?

BRIONY. I'd never trust you.

WILLIAM. If we were down in the forest now, I'd hunt you like an animal. A hundred paces start, and an arrow after you.

BAT. How horrible you are. Your strength was not enough to match against the pettiest spell. My father is right. It is better to be without any heart at all.

BRIONY. How do you know? You never had one.

BAT. Nor ever shall have, now. No feelings ever again. I'll be a sorcerer, greater and darker than my father.
[*To* BRIONY.]
And you shall go to the kitchen!
[*Then he points maliciously at* POPPI.]

And you to a cooking-pot!

POPPI. Me?

BAT. Indeed you. And a fine stew you'll make, too . . . with some onions!

BRIONY. How dare you!

POPPI [*incredulous*]. Me? With onions!

WILLIAM. And what do you suggest for me?

BAT. You will be turned into a Shadow Owl, to hunt the ghosts of fireflies up and down the glades of the forest . . . and never catch one! Fine hunting you'll have then!

WILLIAM. Come nearer!

BAT. Not I, your hands are strong! Maybe you'll become a snake, to drape the body of one of my father's slaves. To bite and crush, if the creature is tardy over his errands. Fine hunting there, too!

WILLIAM. I wish I could hunt you!

BAT. As for your falcon . . .

[*He goes over to the bird.*]

He is beautiful. Ah, he would snatch at me with that long beak.

[*He has drawn his hand back swiftly from the bird whose movement has been masked by his body.*]

WILLIAM. He struck too soon. A pity. He was impatient.

BAT. How he stares at me, with those wild eyes. He is asking me to . . . put my hand closer. . . . Oh no, my bird! You betrayed yourself. What now? You change your thought. You want me to let you go.

WILLIAM. Stop teasing my falcon, will you!

BAT [*to the bird*]. I will free you.

WILLIAM. You'll do what?

BAT. You think I can't? Well, you're wrong. I could let you all go, if I wanted to! And I would have done it, in spite of my father . . . if you had not turned on me so! And all for a minor spell. I'd not help you now, for anything you could say. I'll be glad when my father gets you to the castle, and makes magic with you. I shall laugh. He'll approve my laughter then.

WILLIAM. I wish you would come nearer.

BAT. I'll free the falcon now, to show you how easy it is. He, at least, has never hurt me. He is only a bird.

> Slacken staples, loosen wall,
> Bars open, chains fall,
> Turn the lock without a key,
> Falcon, you are free.

[*The chain round the bird's foot slides away with a clatter. The bars on the door move slowly aside without the door opening, and the falcon spreads his wings and glides out.*]

Finian is free in the night.

[*The bars close again.*]

WILLIAM. If only *I* were!

BAT. You have warned me what you would do.

POPPI. Let us go, Bat. Poppi wants to go home, he's hungry.

[*For a moment*, BAT *looks uncertain, his eyes on* POPPI.]

WILLIAM [*tactlessly*]. If you let me go, I'll promise not to hunt you this time.

BAT. How kind you are! [*He laughs angrily.*] And you so keen a hunter! How does it feel to stand trapped— soon to be destroyed! And still he will not credit sorcery! Though he can do nothing against it, for all his height and strength. Oh, Huntsman, it is not easy to hunt magic.

BRIONY. Stop laughing at him, you hateful thing!

BAT. Why? Do you like him?

BRIONY. What's that to you. How could you understand?

BAT [*mockingly*]. Poor Briony, you'll lose him, soon. How sad to love a shadow or a snake! But you'll soon forget him, as you've forgotten your friendship for me. . . .

BRIONY. For you! You're nothing but a malicious, spiteful, odious goblin! And I hate you!

> [*She brushes past him, almost in tears, and takes refuge with* POPPI *on the hearth, her arms about his neck. But, without intention, she has pushed* BAT *near enough for* WILLIAM *to seize his shoulder, and hold him tightly.*]

WILLIAM. You came too near at last.

BAT. Let me go, will you!

POPPI. Don't cry, Briony. I was that hot, you're making me steam!

WILLIAM. Tell me how to unlock these chains, or I'll wring your neck!

POPPI. Oh, don't let him wring Bat!

BRIONY. I don't care what he does.

WILLIAM. You'd better tell me!

POPPI. *I* can tell you. I've just remembered. Listen, I'll do it to me.

> Slacken staples, loosen wall,
> Bars open, chains fall,
> Turn the lock without a key,
> Poppi, you are free!

[60]

[*The collar slides off his neck, and the bars in the doorway slide apart again.*]

See?

WILLIAM. Oh . . . well, can you free me, too?

POPPI [*excited*]. Yis, yis . . . listen now . . .

> Slacken staples, loosen wall,
> Bars stay open . . . chains fall,
> Turn the lock without a key,
> Huntsman, you are free.

[*The chains fall from* WILLIAM'S *wrists, and he stands free, but he retains a grip of* BAT, *who is still and watchful.*]

WILLIAM [*handsomely*]. I'm sorry I shot an arrow at you, Poppi. I really do apologize.

POPPI. I didn't mind. You missed.

BRIONY. Oh, please let's go, quickly . . . before the Sorcerer comes back. He will, at any moment . . .

POPPI. Yis . . . with onions!

WILLIAM. I'd like to settle a score with these spell-makers, who frighten girls and puppies. And I've no liking for being chained to a wall by a mad old mountebank . . .

BRIONY. Oh, don't. You mustn't stay here.

WILLIAM. You run home.

BRIONY. I won't leave you. You speak too lightly of sorcery. Come away, now.

WILLIAM. Shall I let this one go without reprisal?

BRIONY. He'll have reprisal enough, when his father finds us gone. Leave him here.

BAT. No, I must come with you.

WILLIAM. With us?

BAT. I could have called my father before this . . . but I have stayed silent. . . .

[61]

WILLIAM. You were afraid to call out.

BAT. Fool, before you had hurt me I could have filled this cave with your enemies. I kept quiet because. . . because . . . I don't know why. But you mustn't leave me here, after this!

WILLIAM. We certainly will.

POPPI. Oh . . . let him come. I feel uncomfortable when Bat's bullied.

BAT. My father will be dreadful to face. I cannot stay here. . . .

WILLIAM. Serves you right. I don't pity you. Briony, start quickly. We must go now.

[*She goes to the doorway,* WILLIAM *scowls at* BAT.]
And you'll stay here without moving. If you make any attempt to follow us . . . if I see you again tonight in the forest . . . you know what to expect. An arrow in the moonlight, and that's all you'll find outside.

[*He releases* BAT, *who stands still leaning against the wall, and he goes to join* BRIONY *at the doorway. He turns, to say to* BAT;
Tell your father my name is William, if he is in a mood for conversation. Take my hand, Briony . . . the path is all rocky down the mountain.

BRIONY. Yes, William.

[*She puts her hand in his, and they go out together. She calls* POPPI *over her shoulder.*]
Don't delay, Poppi, or speak to Bat. He belongs here and always did.

[*When the others are gone,* POPPI *crosses to look doubtfully at* BAT, *who has not moved.*]

POPPI. I'm going, Bat. Going home to Mother Hen-wife, *not* into a stew-pot.

[BAT *does not move or answer.* POPPI *looks up at him closely.*]

Not into a stew-pot, do you hear.

BAT [*dully*]. I was teasing you, only.

POPPI. You always do.

BAT. Poppi . . .

[*He rouses himself a little.*]

I'm afraid to be left here alone.

POPPI. So am I. Of onions in a pot.

BAT. I dare not go down into the forest . . . William would kill me . . . and there is nowhere else to run to. My father will easily find me again. I wish I could be less afraid. I learned terror too young. An arrow would be quicker and less terrible than his punishment—yet if I stay here I may grow used to it in time. . . . What shall I do?

POPPI. Dunno.

BAT. Don't go, Poppi. I'll see that no harm comes to you. I'll be kind to you, always, if you stay with me.

POPPI. Your father won't.

BAT. I'll take all the blame for the escape of the others. I'll do whatever he wants of me, if he'll allow me one friend in the castle.

POPPI. Yis . . . but I'm not a friend.

BAT. You are. You must be!

POPPI. I . . . don't know. I feel odd. Hot and steamy! I don't like it. . . . I must run away.

BAT. Stay with me, Poppi, stay with me!

POPPI. I'm going to cry, I am. Bad Bat, making Poppi cry! I don't like you . . . I don't . . . I don't! And the others are out of sight . . . but I can run faster than foxes. Let me go, or I'll singe your fingers!

[63]

BAT. Oh . . . he's coming, now.

[*The thudding of the* SORCERER'S *footsteps can be heard as he approaches, through the archway, right.* BAT *looks at* POPPI *for a moment, then gives him a push.*]

Run . . . go quickly!

[POPPI *races away through the parted bars of the doorway, and vanishes into the darkness of the forest.* BAT *stands listening with growing terror to the sound of his father's approach.*

CURTAIN

IN THE HENWIFE'S COTTAGE

The HUNTSMEN, RUNARD, *is eating porridge rather glumly
out of a wooden bowl. The* HENWIFE *is standing by the
window, looking out, anxiously. She sighs.*

HENWIFE. More?

RUNARD. No, we've had quite enough, thank you,
mistress.

HENWIFE. Both of you?

RUNARD. Both of us.

HENWIFE. What a pity the spell worked this way
round.

RUNARD. How come?

HENWIFE. If only you were both in Rufus, instead of both being in Reynard. It seems to me that Rufus is brave . . . while Reynard . . .

RUNARD. That's right, ma'am, Reynard is a funk.

HENWIFE. So difficult.

RUNARD. (*Ru.*) Very difficult, mistress. The big looby just will not shift.

Want to go home.

HENWIFE. Poor Rufus.

RUNARD. Want to go home . . .

(*Ru.*) Be quiet, you cowardly hulk!

Shan't!

HENWIFE. That's enough. No quarrelling. That will do no good to anyone. Little birds in their nests, you know. And, Reynard, do listen to Rufus and me . . . we can't leave your master in such deadly danger . . . don't you see that?

RUNARD. Serves him right.

HENWIFE. Reynard, how can you!

RUNARD [*sulkily*]. His idea to come here . . . wouldn't go home!

HENWIFE. He could hardly guess that you'd give him to the first Sorcerer you happened to meet!

RUNARD. Serves him right.

HENWIFE. Do stop saying that. If everyone got what they deserve, you'd have a box on the ears! It's more important to save people from getting what they deserve, than to give it to them. Sure you don't want any more?

RUNARD. Quite, thank you.

> [*She takes the bowl from the table, and sets it aside. Then she goes back to the window.*]

HENWIFE. I wish I had a few really strong spells.

But I've never studied more than the simpler forms of white magic. I was not very diligent at school, I'm afraid. And I failed in my certificate. There's just one old and powerful spell in the cupboard, but it must be used only as the very last resource.

RUNARD. When will that be?

HENWIFE. I think I shall know. I asked my hen, Broodie, and all she said was 'wait'. Poor dear, she's rather tetchy tonight. I think Bat must have been teasing her. Her feathers are all sparkling with magic.

> [*She picks the hen out of the basket, and strokes her, gently.*]

RUNARD. The eggs are green! They're duck's eggs.

HENWIFE. Hush, she'll hear you. They're bad, I'm afraid. But how it happened is a mystery. [*The hen clucks.*] What do you say, dear? Magic? Yes, I know. There *has* been rather a lot. Tell me where Briony is now. No, *Briony*, dear. In the forest? Yet you told me before that she was with the Sorcerer . . . Not now? Try to tell me more, dear, do. I'm nearly distraught!

RUNARD. (*Ru.*) We'd better have a look for the girl. No! Are you mad, Rufus! Come back!

> [*He has gone to the door, but runs back to sit down again.*]

(*Ru.*) Get up! You've got to be brave.

Shan't! Want to go home!

(*Ru.*) You're coming with me.

Leave me alone, you bully!

HENWIFE. Stop that! Both of you! There's no use quarrelling among yourselves.

RUNARD. Then what can we do?

HENWIFE. Just wait. And perhaps not so very long. I can hear something . . . out in the forest.

RUNARD. Oooooh!

[*He starts to get under the table. She grabs him.*]

HENWIFE. Rufus, help me with him.

[*Between them, the* HENWIFE *and the* HUNTSMEN *get them all on their feet again, and facing the door.*]

Footsteps . . . but not *his* footsteps! Oh, my dear . . . my dear . . .

[*The door opens, and* BRIONY *enters, followed by* POPPI.]

BRIONY. I'm home, Mother. I'm home and safe!

[*She flings herself into the* HENWIFE'S *arms. The* HENWIFE *smiles, and kisses her, and surreptitiously wipes her eyes.*]

POPPI. Hallo, hallo . . . we're all home.

BRIONY. And William is here, too. Come on in, William.

[*The* BARON *enters, and* BRIONY *takes his hand.*]

WILLIAM. Good evening again, mistress.

HENWIFE. I'm very glad to see you all safe.

RUNARD. My lord!

WILLIAM. I'll have a word with you, later.

RUNARD [*dismally*]. Yes, my lord.

BRIONY. Oh, Mother, I'm so glad to be home.

HENWIFE. Yes, dear. I was a little worried.

[*She is getting out bowls, and stirring up the pot on the fire.*]

POPPI. So were we. Hallo . . . hallo . . . did you miss us?

HENWIFE. Hallo, pet. Yes, indeed, I missed you. Now sit down all of you, and stop chattering. It's such a relief! Now, the porridge is all nice and hot. Set out the bowls, Briony.

BRIONY. Yes, Mother. Sit down, William.

RUNARD. Here, sir.

WILLIAM. Thank you.

> [*He looks coldly at* RUNARD, *who smirks and bows.* WILLIAM *sits at the table, and* BRIONY *sets bowls around.* POPPI *frisks about, and nearly has everyone down on several occasions.*]

HENWIFE. Don't get under my feet so, Poppi. Bless the creature, he nearly had me over! Go and sit by the fire, do! Your supper will be coming.

> [*She serves porridge to* WILLIAM, *while* BRIONY *fetches a large dish marked ' Poppi ' on the side, and when it is filled, takes it to* POPPI. *He gulps loudly at the food.*]

BRIONY. There, Poppi. That's better than being eaten in a stew.

POPPI. Yis!

BRIONY. Mother, they were going to eat Poppi in a . . .

HENWIFE. Sit down, dear, and have your supper first.

BRIONY. It was terrible, Mother.

HENWIFE. I am sure it was, but finish your supper. Have you all you want, William?

WILLIAM. Everything, thank you.

BRIONY. He's a Baron, Mother, but he said we could call him William . . . on account of the dangers we've been through.

POPPI [*gobbling*]. Nice William . . . nice . . . hup! 'Scuse me.

HENWIFE. I met William before, in the forest. Don't eat so fast, Poppi.

> [*She puts her hand to her head.*]

There's something bothering me . . . what is it?

There's a very strong smell of magic . . . you brought
it in with you. Yet, there's no spell working here,
now. Something is wrong, and I can't think what
it is.

BRIONY. We were in the Sorcerer's hunting-lodge. In
the cave on the side of the mountain.

HENWIFE. Have you finished your porridge, dear?

BRIONY. Yes, Mother.

WILLIAM. There are strange creatures in your forest,
mistress.

HENWIFE. There are, indeed.

POPPI. Hup!

> [*The* HENWIFE *looks at him.*]

'Scuse me.

HENWIFE. Take a deep breath, Poppi. I told you not
to gobble so. Have you finished, sir? Would you like
some more?

WILLIAM. Yes, please. It's very good.

HENWIFE. Porridge is excellent, if you're really
hungry. This is the second potful I've made tonight.

> [*She pauses, with her hand to her head, and a worried
> look comes over her face again.*]

BRIONY. Have you a headache, Mother?

HENWIFE. It's that same worry again. Something is
wrong, and there is still a smell of enchantment
round you all. Tell me what happened to you in
the cave? Did he put a spell on you of any kind?

BRIONY. Oh, no, Mother. We escaped before he could
do anything.

POPPI. We ran and ran . . . hup!

HENWIFE. Clap your hands, Briony, dear, and give
him a fright. That will stop his hiccoughs.

BRIONY [*clapping her hands*]. There.

POPPI. Hup! 'Scuse me.

BRIONY. The Sorcerer would have taken me to the castle to be his kitchenmaid . . . for ever, Mother. And Poppi . . .

POPPI. In a stew, with onions!

HENWIFE. How nasty.

BRIONY. And Bat told William he would be turned into a shadow owl . . .

HENWIFE. *Where is Bat?*

BRIONY. To hunt for the ghosts of fireflies . . . what did you say, Mother?

HENWIFE. I said, what have you done with Bat?

   [*A slight pause.* BRIONY *looks bewildered.*]

That's what has troubled me. I was so glad to see you safe, that I forgot he was not here. Where, *where* is he?

   [BRIONY'S *face changes to a cold expression.*]

BRIONY. We left him in the hunting-lodge. But no doubt he will be in the castle by now. The Sorcerer wanted to go back there at midnight.

HENWIFE. Oh, is this true? William, tell me plainly.

WILLIAM. The boy is with his father, certainly.

POPPI. Yis, he can't get away. William said he would kill him, if he escaped again.

HENWIFE. What have you done, all of you?

BRIONY. Mother, is something wrong?

HENWIFE. Very wrong indeed.

WILLIAM. In what way?

HENWIFE. Poppi . . .

POPPI. Hup?

HENWIFE. Why did you let him stay there? You

[71]

should have made him come with you . . . however
he argued. You ought to have forced him away.
Begged him to come . . .

POPPI. But he wanted to. He begged us to take
him.

HENWIFE. What are you telling me?

POPPI. And we wouldn't. William said he would hunt
him in the forest. And I tried to burn him.

HENWIFE. What was the matter with you all?

BRIONY. Are you blaming us, Mother?

HENWIFE. How strange your voice is! And your eyes
are cold.

WILLIAM [*to* BRIONY]. Your mother is a little over-
wrought, I imagine, because of your long absence.
Calm yourself, madam, the young man you call Bat
is safe with his father.

HENWIFE. You think so?

WILLIAM. There seems small cause for your distress
concerning him. A thing without feeling!

HENWIFE. What of yourself? Oh, don't think I've
forgotten you, my hunter! You, who shot an arrow
at Poppi . . . and laughed at my fears!

BRIONY. Don't be harsh on William, Mother. He
brought me safely back here through the forest. He
was right to say what he did about Bat. Bat *is*
inhuman . . . we must hate him . . . kindly feeling
turn to hate . . . I feel very odd.

WILLIAM. Briony, what's the matter!

BRIONY. My hands are tingling . . . I smell magic . . .
I feel as if I've been under a spell. . . .

HENWIFE. The smell of magic!

POPPI. A spell! Yow! [*He howls.*] Hup!

HENWIFE. What is it, Poppi?

[72]

POPPI. I remember, now. A nasty, black spell, to make us hate Bat. And we did. Ow! Yow! Wow! And I tried to burn him . . . Oh, my Bat!

HENWIFE. So that's what went on. Briony, do you remember, too? Come, child, shake yourself free of the venomous magic!

BRIONY. I . . . I don't know what happened.

WILLIAM. This is nonsense. That . . . that puppy thing is crazed about spells. The girl is faint with fatigue, that's all.

HENWIFE. Oh, what shall I do, now!

WILLIAM. What needs doing? Forget the young man.

HENWIFE. What shall I do!

WILLIAM. Reynard, it is time to go home. The moonlight has been seeping into my brain, filling it with dreams of magic, and monsters. I can see that your forest may be dangerous to a dreamer, ma'am . . . but I'm no dreamer. I shall go back to my valley. And return again by daylight, when the nightmares of the dark are forgotten . . . [He smiles at BRIONY.] . . . to see if any good dreams remain.

BRIONY. What are you looking for, Mother?

[The HENWIFE has gone to take her cloak from the back of the door. Now she opens a little cupboard.]

HENWIFE. I hope it has kept fresh, all these years.

[She takes out a small earthenware jar, and puts it in her pocket.]

BRIONY. What are you doing?

HENWIFE. It's useless to tell you, for you're still under a spell, my dear. It has worn off Poppi, and will

[73]

wear off you in time. Just stay here, and finish your supper. . . . William, look after Briony till I come back. [*Rather dazedly.*] I hope I shall be back . . . soon.

> [*She goes over to the door, a small figure wrapped in the feather cloak, her face set and anxious.*]

I'll just see what I can do. I have the spell in a jam-jar.

> [*She goes out.* POPPI *howls, and* BRIONY *crosses to the door.*]

BRIONY. She has taken the path that leads up the mountain.

WILLIAM. She shouldn't be allowed to go.

BRIONY. She is out of sight under the trees. I know she's going to the castle. Why? Why should she care what happens to Bat?

POPPI. I care, too. And I'm going with the Henwife. Hup!

BRIONY. I don't understand! Bat is hateful . . . while the spell shall domineer . . . what am I saying, now? The spell? . . . And prove . . . little value lies in love. *I remember . . .*

WILLIAM. Dear, you're tired, and you've been frightened . . .

BRIONY. I've been enchanted. And Bat is up there alone with the Sorcerer.

WILLIAM. Forget him.

BRIONY. William, come with me.

WILLIAM. Where to?

RUNARD. Don't you listen to her, my lord. Have a heart.

BRIONY. That, please— . . . oh, William, free yourself and come with me to the castle. My mother has gone

[74]

alone, with her one spell. What can she do? What can I do? But I must go.

WILLIAM [*Sensibly*]. Look—wait till daylight, and I'll ride up and enquire if the boy's all right . . . since you are so anxious.

BRIONY. That will be far too late. It may be too late, now.

WILLIAM. Nonsense.

POPPI. I'll come with you, Briony. We'll run fast . . . faster than foxes . . . oh, oh, my Bat . . . do hurry, Briony.

> [*He has run to the door.* BRIONY *stares at* WILLIAM.]

BRIONY. I have been mistaken in you, William. Perhaps the spell that made me think Bat hateful, made me think you kind. I wanted you to come with me, because you are so strong . . . but strength is worse than useless, if it is not merciful. Stay here.

POPPI. And talk to the hens. Hup! 'Scuse me.

RUNARD. (*Ru.*) You go, sir. I'll come, too.
No, we won't! Don't be a fool, Rufus.

> [BRIONY *still watches* WILLIAM, *with a faint hope, but he suddenly breaks out.*]

WILLIAM. You can say I'm under a spell, or any nonsense you please. But I'll not climb the mountain again, to talk to a madman, and his mongrel son! A henwife . . . a young girl . . . and a talking puppy! You're all moonstruck! Briony, why are you looking at me like that?

> [BRIONY *backs away from him with horror.*]

BRIONY. Oh, the smell of magic! Your voice is like that of the Sorcerer . . . and I can see snakes in your eyes!

[75]

[*With a small cry she turns and runs out of the door.* POPPI *races after her, with a loud ' Hup '* WILLIAM *stares after them, and raises his hands to his eyes.*]

WILLIAM. Am I under a spell, indeed?

CURTAIN

IN THE SORCERER'S CASTLE

There is a tall, arched window upstage, right, with bars across it. A doorway, left, flanked with slender pillars, that have snakes coiled round them. At the back is a throne-like and sinister chair, on a dais. At either side of the chair are pedestals six feet high, and from the top of these rises a faint coil of smoke, caused by the burning of something magic. Moonlight streams through the window on to the tall and rigid figure of the SORCERER.

BAT is sitting on the ground, leaning his head against the side of the throne. His eyes are closed.

HEMLOCK. Have you made up your mind?
       [BAT *moves his head a little, but does not answer.*]

[77]

To continue this opposition is sheer stupidity. Enough, do what I tell you.

[*A pause.* HEMLOCK *makes an angry gesture.*]
You have watched me rouse the storms that shook the mountain. You cowered when the lightning flew like swords. I can teach that power to you.

BAT. I have the power. I can make a storm.

HEMLOCK. Only a local one. I can show you how to make such a tempest that it will flood the land, and crush the trees as though they were grass. . . .

BAT. Why should I wish to?

HEMLOCK. To cause fear and pain.

BAT [*Shaking his head*]. I have felt fear and pain.

HEMLOCK [*furiously*]. It should not be possible for you to do so! You will feel no further qualms when you accept my rule again. Do you understand?

BAT. I understand what you say.

HEMLOCK. Why do you anger me so? I can force you to obey. It is a waste of time to resist.

BAT. Then why batter me with words?

HEMLOCK. Listen to me, Bat. Look at me.

[*He goes closer to his son, but* BAT *turns his head away further.* HEMLOCK *raises his hand, as though he would strike* BAT. *Then he changes his mind, and crosses to the window again. He looks out.*]
Fool, do you know what you are risking? If I force you under my power . . . if I make you my slave by magic . . . you will be as mindless as the creatures of the forest whom I have hunted and transformed into my servants. With your free consent I will put power in your hands and leave you a mind to exult in it.

[*There is a pause.*]

[78]

BAT. Why are you so eager to give me power?

HEMLOCK. You are my son.

BAT. That can mean nothing to you.

HEMLOCK. Not in human terms. But I wish to see you made into my image.

BAT. I might grow stronger than you.

HEMLOCK. That would be impossible. I am eternal power. Obey me.

[*A pause.*]

I am waiting for your answer.

[*Another pause.*]

I should have made you swear obedience years ago, but I had no use for a mere boy. . . . I left it too long. How could I guess you would run and find refuge with the Henwife. All your life you have spent here with me, how could I guess you still retained the seeds of feeling?

[*He looks down out of the window.*]

And you climbed down this creeper to the foot of the tower, and escaped in the daylight. You'll not do that again. I've a mind to wither the roots and the tendrils . . . here and now . . .

[*He raises his head and looks at the sky.*]

All the elements will obey me . . . but not my son.

> Cloud and mist, and middle air,
> Wake the thunder from its lair;
> Let the lightning's jagged spears
> Dull the glitter of the stars;
> Let the winds take tongue and form,
> Hunt like hounds beside the storm!

[*Outside the window, there is a roar of thunder, and a flicker of lightning. A wind begins to howl.*]

At least I am lord of Unicorn Mountain, and the

F

elements that surround the peaks. My servants lie coiled everywhere in my castle, and wait for my commands.

[*He crosses to* BAT *and looks fiercely at him.*]

No more delay. The hour is running out to meet midnight.

BAT. My mind is misted over.

HEMLOCK. You're stupid!

BAT. Yes—yis—I know.

[*His face twists, as he remembers Poppi.* HEM-LOCK *watches closely.*]

HEMLOCK. Ah—why torture yourself, my son? In surrendering, you only give up the misery and heart-ache. No one but a fool can wish to be hurt twice—

BAT. I can make no further argument. Tell me what to do.

HEMLOCK. Turn, and look at me.

[BAT *turns his head wearily.*]

This is all that you need say:

All the heart that I have gained,
All the feeling so obtained,
Take away, and give instead
Only power in hand and head.

BAT. And after?

HEMLOCK. This.

[*He lifts a short, thick sword with a jewelled hilt from the hook on the wall down right, where it has been hanging.*]

BAT [*tonelessly*]. To kill me?

HEMLOCK. How can it kill you? You will have no heart at all once you have said that spell. It is a mere precaution, for what this cold steel touches remains cold forever. Are you afraid?

BAT. No.

HEMLOCK. It will not even hurt. Speak as I told you.

> [HEMLOCK *grimly crosses to stand beside* BAT, *who rises a little.* HEMLOCK *raises his hand, with the sword in it.*]

Now.

BAT.   All the heart that I have gained,
             All the feeling . . .

What is that?

HEMLOCK. Go on! Go on! Why do you wait?

BAT.   All the feeling so obtained. . . .

Who called my name?

HEMLOCK. Will no one ever finish any of my spells!

BAT [*rising to his feet*]. Someone is calling.

HEMLOCK. Who could call you in this place? Come back!

> [BAT *evades his hand, and goes swiftly to the window.*]

BAT. Someone climbing the creeper.

HEMLOCK. What!

> [BRIONY *appears on the ledge outside, clinging to the edge of the window.*]

BAT. Briony!

BRIONY. Are you safe, Bat? Where is the Sorcerer?

> [POPPI *appears beside her on the window-ledge, rather out of breath.*]

POPPI. Hup!

HEMLOCK. I am here.

> [POPPI *starts to hiccup, and nearly chokes, but the shock is effective, for he does not do it again.*]

             Bars divide,
             Open wide.

[*The bars on the window draw aside.*]

Was that the little spell you used for your escape, Bat? Come in, my dears, you are welcome. Help our guest to enter, my son.

> [BAT *gives his hand to* BRIONY, *and she comes nervously through the window, followed by* POPPI.]

BAT. Why have you come back?

BRIONY. To find you, Bat.

BAT. How stupid!

> [*He turns his back on her, frowning, and crosses to stand beside his father.* BRIONY *looks puzzled, and* HEMLOCK *laughs, and puts a hand on* BAT'S *shoulder.*]

HEMLOCK. You will find him considerably changed, my dear. I have been reasoning with him.

BRIONY. What have you done?

HEMLOCK. He is my son again.

BRIONY. Then we're too late? Poppi . . . come away . . .

> [*They turn, and would escape by the window.*]

HEMLOCK. Do you think to escape so easily?

> At my command,
> Obey my hand.

> [*The* SORCERER *beckons with his hand, and* POPPI *and* BRIONY *turn, and then come slowly towards him, as he summons them. They move stiffly.* BAT *goes aside, and watches.*]

> Now, at my bidding, learn
> To turn again . . . and turn . . .

> [POPPI *and* BRIONY *turn round, and weave slow circles about the room, obeying the movements of the* SORCERER'S *hands.*]

BAT. Oh, no! It's horrible to see them!

[82]

HEMLOCK. Horrible? To you? Ah, you have not yet spoken your words.

> Be still.

> At my will.

[*His victims stop turning, and remain quite still, except that* BRIONY *puts her hands to her head.*]

BRIONY. How giddy I am.

HEMLOCK. You've escaped lightly. For you interrupted some great magic. Bat, have you forgotten what to say?

BAT. No.

HEMLOCK. Come under my sword.

[*He raises the sword, and* BAT *crosses to stand beside him.*]

BRIONY. What are you doing?

HEMLOCK. He is accepting sorcery.

BRIONY. Bat—no!

BAT. You left me here with him.

BRIONY. It was not my fault. . . . I came back to find you.

BAT. Why?

BRIONY. My Mother loves you. . . . I also. You are like my brother.

HEMLOCK. That is perfectly understandable, because as it happens, Briony, he is your brother.

[*A pause.* BRIONY *and* BAT *stare at each other for a moment, then look at* HEMLOCK *in amazement.*]

You find it hard to believe, but it's true. There was a time when white magic and black were all one. And all white. I found greater powers for myself, and your mother ran away from the castle, and hid herself behind the guard of her own spells. But I managed to keep my son here.

BRIONY. Then . . . you're my father?

[83]

[HEMLOCK *smiles and she covers her face with her hands.*]

Oh . . .

[BAT *moves towards her.*]

POPPI. Never mind, Briony, we'll just forget it.

HEMLOCK. Bat, take no heed of her. The spell is still unspoken.

BAT. I . . . I have . . . forgotten the words.

HEMLOCK [*furiously*]. *She* made you forget! She is wholly human, for she was gone from here before I gave up my humanity. And you . . . you are more vulnerable than I supposed. Very well, I shall use that failing in you to enforce my commands. Will you see your sister turned into a serpent? Hissing and brainless, and slavish?

BAT. You would do that?

HEMLOCK. You shall see it happen, unless you obey. And as for this creature . . .

POPPI [*dismally*]. To the stew-pot, with onions.

HEMLOCK. An excellent idea. Your obedience can save them. And then, when you have learned your lessons, I may offer like power to Briony. She shall be the Witch of Unicorn Mountain.

BRIONY. I won't.

HEMLOCK. Better that than a serpent. The choice is yours, Bat.

BAT. I don't know what to do . . .

HEMLOCK. Speak the spell.

BRIONY. Mother would never let you!

BAT [*lifting his head*]. But she is not here to tell me what to do.

BRIONY. I'll speak for her. Listen, Bat, this is what she always sang to you:

[84]

The cottage is warm, the fire is bright,
Who would want to go out in the night?
Who would want moonlight, and magic, and
    fear . . .

HEMLOCK. What childish house-magic is this to set against me?

POPPI. Let Briony sing to Bat!

HEMLOCK. She'll be a serpent in the tick of a second! And as for you . . .

    [*He advances threateningly on* POPPI.]

POPPI.   At my command,
         Obey my hand!

    [*He holds up his paw, and* HEMLOCK *stops suddenly.*]

HEMLOCK. You'll regret that!

    [*He touches the snake's head on his crown.*]

         Touch snake,
         Spell break.

    [*He moves towards* POPPI *again, who retreats backwards and growls.*]

How dare you play tricks on me, puppy! We'll see how many spells you remember, in a stew-pot!

BRIONY. You mustn't cook Poppi! Let him go. Please.

HEMLOCK. That is for Bat to decide. Are you going to save them both by obeying?

BAT. I must.

HEMLOCK. You know the spell!

    [BAT *puts his hands to his head, desperately.*]

BAT. All . . . all the . . . the feeling . . . no . . . all the heart . . .

HEMLOCK. Must I force you to remember?

    [*He moves threatingly towards* BAT. POPPI *growls, and shouts at him;*

[85]

POPPI.   Now, at my bidding, learn
                 To turn again . . . and turn!
               [*He waves his hands, and the* SORCERER *spins round. This is a horrifying effect, and* BRIONY *is terrified.*]

BRIONY. You shouldn't anger him more!

POPPI. I like spinning him. Look.
               [*He waves his hands faster, and the* SORCERER *roars with rage. The room darkens, and green lights begin to flicker. The* SORCERER *touches his crown again.*]

HEMLOCK.   Touch snake,
                 Spell break!
               [*He stops turning, and stands still. The* HENWIFE *appears in the doorway. A pause.*]

HEMLOCK. How have you entered my castle?

HENWIFE. By my one great spell, Hemlock. And all your slaves are asleep, and will not wake till I release them.

HEMLOCK. Your one spell? And it is used. I can destroy you all by any one of my million spells.

HENWIFE. But you shall not enslave my son.
               [BAT *moves towards her, but* HEMLOCK *catches him by the wrist.* BRIONY *runs across to her mother, and hides her face on her shoulder.*]

BRIONY. I am afraid.

HENWIFE. Come away from him, Bat.

BAT. He holds me.

HENWIFE. Oh, if only I were stronger. To have come so far, and still be helpless against force.
               [HEMLOCK *stands on the dais before his great chair, and looks down at them all, still holding* BAT.]

HEMLOCK. For the last time, Bat, will you accept my authority?

HENWIFE. No!

BAT. No.

HEMLOCK. Then, Henwife, you have killed your son. It is you who will grieve, for I have no feelings.

[*He raises his sword.*]

This will sink into whatever heart you have given him.

HENWIFE. Can you be nothing but cruelty?

[*She goes across to* HEMLOCK, *and raises her hands to deflect the blade. He brushes her aside.*]

HEMLOCK. You have no strength against me. Love must be armed to fight against a sword.

[WILLIAM *appears in the doorway with drawn sword. He rushes in, and strikes up the blade in* HEMLOCK'S *raised hand.*]

HENWIFE. I hoped that you would come.

[*She moves back to* BRIONY, *and puts her arms round her.*]

WILLIAM. Reynard, watch for his servants.

[REYNARD *has appeared at the door, very out of breath.*]

HEMLOCK. No human can fight with me, and triumph!

[*He attacks* WILLIAM, *who parries him, and they disengage.*]

HENWIFE. If you kill him, William, he will turn into a hawk.

WILLIAM. I've shot a hawk.

HEMLOCK. You can never shoot me.

[*He attacks* WILLIAM *again, and they fight, circling about the room.* BRIONY *hides her face, and* POPPI *crouches near the window.* BAT *is leaning dazedly against the throne.*]

[87]

My life is hidden safely where no one shall ever find it.

[HEMLOCK *suddenly stabs at* BAT, *and* WILLIAM *in deflecting this, leaves himself unguarded, and* HEMLOCK *wounds him in the shoulder.* BRIONY *cries out.* WILLIAM *staggers and moves down, right, and* BAT *goes swiftly to support him.*]

POPPI [*while this is happening*]. Oh! Look out!

HEMLOCK [*as he thrusts*]. You're easily distracted.

[*He laughs, pauses a moment, then moves down towards* WILLIAM.]

I conquer easily.

BAT. I can heal the wound.

POPPI. Get back! Leave William alone.

[*He rushes at the* SORCERER, *his tail glowing red-hot.* BAT *makes a movement with his hand and lays it on the wound.*]

HEMLOCK [*to* POPPI]. Get out of my way!

RUNARD. (*Ru.*) Come on, Reynard, grab the sword! No, it's sharp.

(*Ru.*) Coward! Be quick!

[RUNARD *intercepts* HEMLOCK, *then springs back with a yell.*]

I won't, I won't!

(*Ru.*) Yes, you will! Come on!

HEMLOCK. How many of you are there?

POPPI. I'll burn you, singe you, fry you, bake you! Don't you touch my William.

[*The* SORCERER *burns himself on* POPPI, *and yells with fury. But* WILLIAM *is recovered, and now moves into action again.*]

HEMLOCK [*to* POPPI]. I'll cut you in half!

WILLIAM. Out of the way, Poppi! Do you hear!

POPPI. Oooh . . . yis!

[88]

[WILLIAM *heels* POPPI *out of harm's way, and attacks* HEMLOCK.]

HEMLOCK. You press me too hard! Keep back! I'll put a spell on you . . .

HENWIFE. Your spells are useless, for your servants are asleep.

HEMLOCK. I am not afraid. No one can kill me, for my life is too well hidden.

[*He backs to the window and* WILLIAM *stabs him. He falls with a cry.*]

HENWIFE. He will turn into a hawk. Be careful, or he'll escape you yet!

[WILLIAM *and* RUNARD *seize the Sorcerer's cloak, masking his body. Now there is a flash, and the* SORCERER *has vanished.*]

WILLIAM. It was a hawk that flew away!

HENWIFE. You can never destroy him now.

BRIONY. Yes . . . yes . . .

[*She runs to the window, and leans out.*]

Finian! Finian! Call him, William!

WILLIAM. Finian!

[*He gives a whistle out of the window.*]

BRIONY. Oh, listen! The falcon is diving.

[*There is a rush of wings outside, and a thump. Something hurtles in through the window, and* POPPI *catches it.*]

RUNARD. What was that!

HENWIFE. The egg. Your falcon killed the hawk, and the life of the Sorcerer escaped again, in the form of an egg. It fell in here, through the window. His life is in the egg.

WILLIAM. Well, where is it?

BRIONY. Poppi caught it.

[89]

POPPI. Yis, caught it! Nasty big, white egg!

HENWIFE. What did you do with it?

WILLIAM. Give it to me.

POPPI. Poppi sat on it.

> [*He takes it from under him. It is now bright red.*]

Here you are. It's red-hot. I've hard-boiled it.

> [*He hands it to* WILLIAM, *who burns his hands, and shouts with surprise, hurling it into the fire, where it explodes. A pause.*]

HENWIFE. Poor Hemlock, he always tried to be too clever.

> [*She crosses to* BAT. RUNARD *has backed to the window when the egg exploded, and now* RUFUS *is standing beside him.*]

Good evening, Rufus. I'm glad to see you again.

WILLIAM. Where have you been?

REYNARD. Here, my lord.

RUFUS. Here, my lord.

REYNARD. Who said that? You!

> [*He flings his arms round* RUFUS, *who recoils.*]

RUFUS. Here, steady on! Look out, do. It'll happen again.

REYNARD. It won't.

RUFUS. It will.

HENWIFE. It won't! The spells of Hemlock are all broken.

REYNARD. I'm absolutely beside myself.

WILLIAM. Forgive me, ma'am. I nearly came too late.

HENWIFE. Ah, but you did come.

> [*She takes hold of the snake on* BAT'S *tunic, by the head, and unwinds it easily.*]

There.

> [*She looks at the snake.*]

It's asleep. Poor thing. It can't have liked being a belt. Now it can go free. Bat, you must make white magic here, to free all the forest. You'll do that, dear, won't you?

BAT. I'll try.

HENWIFE. Well, I'll keep an eye on you.

[*She smiles at him, and lifts the green hair from his head, leaving only yellow.*]

WILLIAM. He looks quite human . . . I beg your pardon, Bat, I do, really.

[BAT *laughs, and gives his hand to* WILLIAM *amicably.*]

BAT. You must come back to the forest and the mountain, William. This castle shall be your hunting-lodge, whenever you want it.

WILLIAM. I'm not sure about that. It makes you think, once you have been the quarry.

HENWIFE. I always felt he could be sensible, in spite of himself.

BAT. But I'll make magic for you, William. Harmless magic. I can give you dream unicorns to hunt . . . and the shadows of eagles for your falcon to stoop at. You may have such fantastic creatures for your chase as would satisfy Orion. With all the excitement of the hunt, and no hurt at the finish.

BRIONY. But . . . William doesn't believe in magic.

BAT. He does, now.

[BRIONY *crosses to look up into* WILLIAM'S *face. The light is growing stronger outside the window.*]

WILLIAM. Can you see snakes, Briony?

BRIONY. No. I see . . .

[*She drops her head, shyly.*]

[91]

I see that you do believe, at last.

HENWIFE. Well, that's all perfectly splendid. And the day is breaking.

> [*They look at the window, where the light is still growing.* RUFUS *holds his hand out through the parted bars, and gives a whistle. Then he draws back his arm, with Finian clinging to his hand.*]

[*sighing*]. Dear me, what a very fatiguing night we've had.

BAT. You shouldn't climb mountains, Mother, on a night of full moon.

> [*She slaps his wrist lightly, and he laughs. He takes her over to the throne, and helps her on to the dais.*]

You can rest now. Unicorn Mountain is at peace.

> [*She takes her place on the throne, with* BAT *leaning against the back at her right.* BRIONY *is on the left, holding* WILLIAM *by the hand. The* HUNTSMEN *are stroking Finian in the window embrasure.* POPPI *runs to* BAT, *and sits at his feet, yawning loudly.*]

HENWIFE. Oh, what a relief to sit down.

CURTAIN